Get set for the Maths SATS with CGP!

This brilliant CGP book is filled to the brim with realistic SATS-style questions for the tests in 2017 and beyond!

It covers the core foundations of KS2 Maths — perfect for students who are working towards the expected standard.

We've even included Practice Tests at the start and end of the book, so you can easily measure how much progress they've made!

What CGP is all about

Our sole aim here at CGP is to produce the highest quality books — carefully written, immaculately presented and dangerously close to being funny.

Then we work our socks off to get them out to you — at the cheapest possible prices.

Contents

Section Four — Measure

Section Five — Geometry

Section Six — Statistics

Published by CGP

Editors:
Katie Braid, Robin Flello, Shaun Harrogate and Jonathan Wray

ISBN: 978 1 78294 757 8

With thanks to Tina Ramsden and Caley Simpson for the proofreading.
Also thanks to Ana Pungartnik for the copyright research.

Thumb illustration used throughout the book © iStock.com

Contains public sector information licensed under the Open Government Licence v3.0.
http://www.nationalarchives.gov.uk/doc/open-government-licence/version/3/

Printed by Elanders Ltd, Newcastle upon Tyne.
Clipart from Corel®

Based on the classic CGP style created by Richard Parsons.

About This Book

This Book is Full of KS2 Maths Questions

At the end of Year 6, you'll be tested on all the maths you've learnt during Key Stage 2.

This book has questions on the core topics you might be tested on.
There are warm-up questions to help you get started with some topics and guided questions to help you answer the more difficult questions.

This book also has two Practice Tests.
The one at the front of the book is to test how much you already know.
The test at the back of the book is to see how much more you can do after using this book.

The answers to all of the questions are at the back of this book.

This book covers the key Learning Objectives from the KS2 National Curriculum.

This Book Matches Our Foundation Revision Book

The Foundation Revision Book can help you if you get stuck.
It explains the core maths topics that are likely to come up on your test.
It's also got guided examples to show you how to answer test questions.

There are Learning Objectives on All Pages

Learning objectives say what you should be able to do.
Use the tick circles to show how confident you feel.

Tick here if you think you need a bit more practice.

If you're really struggling, tick here.

Tick this circle if you can do all the maths on the page.

"I can calculate using negative numbers."

Practice Test 1

1 Look at the number 547.26

Which digit is in the **hundreds** place?

1 mark

Which digit is in the **tenths** place?

1 mark

2 Shade in $\frac{2}{5}$ of this shape.

1 mark

3 Work out 7621 + 1290.

1 mark

4 Circle **one** prime number in the list below.

   6   11   15   21

1 mark

5 This bar chart shows the number of different desserts a restaurant sold one evening.

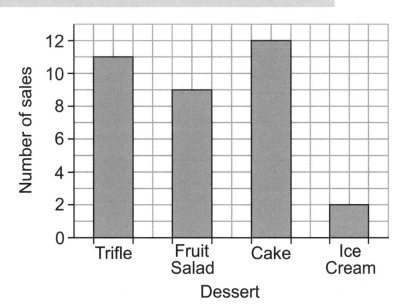

How many **more** trifles were sold than ice creams?

2 marks

6 Use this number line to help you work out these calculations.

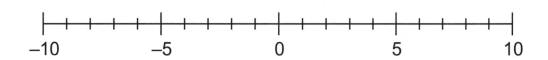

$-6 + 8 =$

$6 - 11 =$

2 marks

7 Circle the net which will fold up to make a cube.

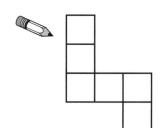 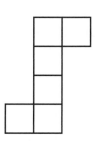 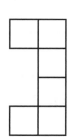 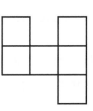

1 mark

Practice Test 1

4

8 Put these numbers in order starting with the **smallest**.

88 300   84 100   86 400

Smallest		Largest

1 mark

9 Round:

820 to the **nearest 100**.   62 820 to the **nearest 1000**.

2 marks

10 A shape is shown on the grid below.

Translate the shape +6 units horizontally and –5 units vertically.

1 mark

What are the coordinates of point A on the **translated shape**?

(___ , ___)

1 mark

11 Calculate the size of **angle m** on the diagram below.

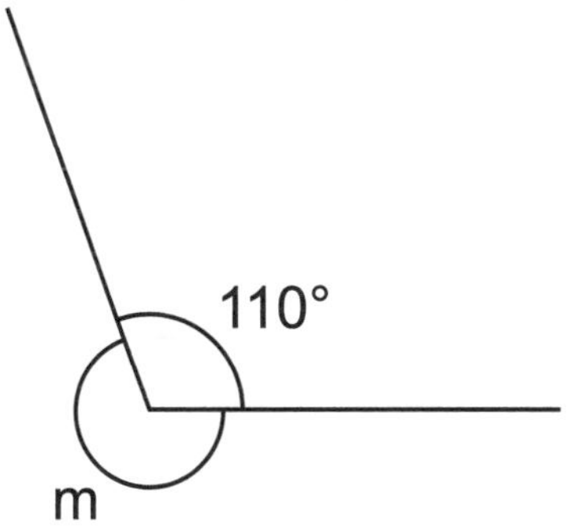

110°

m

○

1 mark

12 1130 sticks are divided equally between 6 campfires.

How many whole sticks will be in each campfire?

1 mark

How many whole sticks will be **left over**?

1 mark

13 Work out 30% of 60.

2 marks

Total

Practice Test 1

Place Value

1 Look at the number 9750.

Which **digit** is in the hundreds place?

1 mark

Which **digit** is in the ones place?

1 mark

2 In the number 25 473, the 7 represents 70.

What does the 4 represent?

1 mark

What does the 2 represent?

1 mark

3 Write eight thousand and forty six as a **number**.

1 mark

Place Value

4 Write 9210 in **words**.

1 mark

5 Circle all the numbers that have an 8 in the **thousands** place.

6854	8972	786 542
128 547	94 280	38 083

1 mark

6 Monib has one hundred and twenty three thousand, eight hundred and fifteen emails in his inbox.

Write this amount as a **number**.

1 mark

7 Write the number 210 263 in **words**.

1 mark

"I can read and write numbers up to hundred thousands, and work out the value of each digit."

Section One — Number & Place Value

Ordering Numbers

1 Circle the **smallest** number in the list below.

252   298   246   258

1 mark

2 Which of these numbers is the **largest**?

5311   6292   6322   6280   6305

1 mark

3 Write < or > in each box to make these number sentences correct.

923 ☐ 955   5280 ☐ 5264

1 mark

4 Write these numbers in order starting with the **largest**.

8210   8120   8260

☐   ☐   ☐

Largest   **Smallest**

1 mark

Ordering Numbers

5 The prices of four sports cars are shown below.
£96 200   £99 300   £90 600   £88 900

Put the values in order starting with **lowest value**.

Lowest   £

£

£

Highest   £

6 Put these numbers in order starting with the **largest**.

232 200   260 600   222 300   268 900

Largest

Smallest

"I can order and compare numbers
up to hundred thousands."

Section One — Number & Place Value

Negative Numbers

(1) Work out each of these calculations.

The number line below can help you.

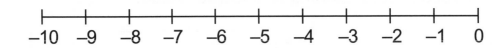

−5 + 3 = [ ]   −2 − 7 = [ ]

[ ] **2 marks**

(2) Work out these calculations.

The number line below can help you.

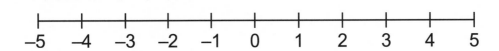

−2 + 4 = [ ]   5 − 8 = [ ]

[ ] **2 marks**

(3) Work out the following calculations.

The number line below can help you.

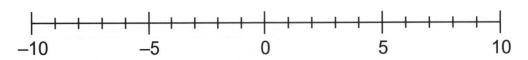

−8 + 9 = [ ]   3 − 10 = [ ]

[ ] **2 marks**

Negative Numbers

4 A number line is shown below. Find the missing number.

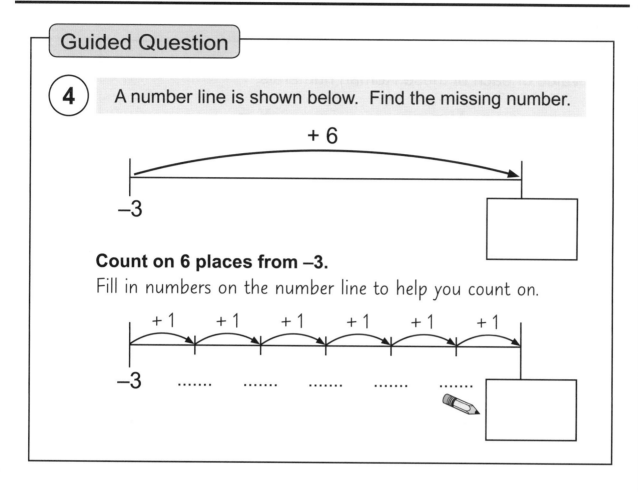

Count on 6 places from −3.

Fill in numbers on the number line to help you count on.

1 mark

5 Two number lines are shown below.
Write the missing numbers in the boxes.

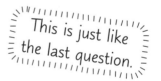
This is just like the last question.

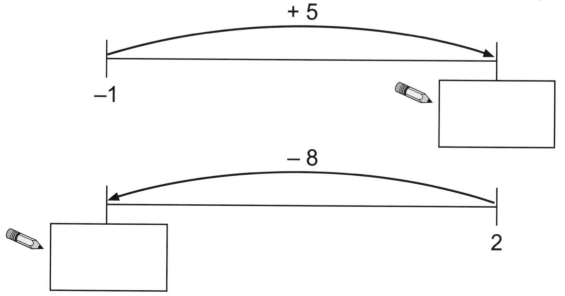

1 mark

1 mark

"I can calculate using negative numbers."

Roman Numerals

Warm up

Write the value of each of these Roman numerals.

I = ... V = ... X = ...

L = ... C = ...

1 What are the values of these Roman numerals?

XVI LXXV

2 marks

2 Circle the **two** Roman numerals that are less than 50.

XC XL CVI XXIV

2 marks

3 Draw lines to match these Roman numerals with their values.

CXV	95
XCV	105
CV	115

2 marks

"I can read Roman numerals up to C."

Decimals

1 Look at the number 96.37

Which digit is in the **tenths** place?

1 mark

Which digit is in the **hundredths** place?

1 mark

2 In the number 164.75, the value of the 7 is 0.7

What is the value of the 5?

1 mark

3 Write the decimals marked by arrows on these number lines.

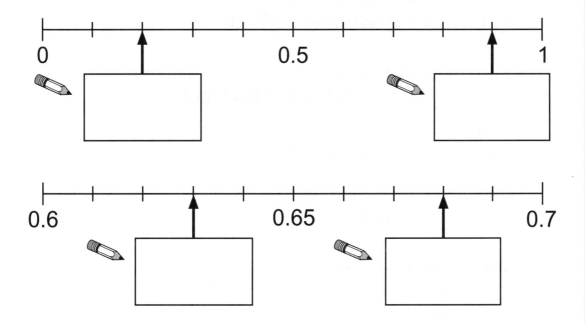

1 mark

1 mark

"I can identify the value of each digit to two decimal places."

Section One — Number & Place Value

Ordering Decimals

1 Write **<** or **>** in each box to make these number sentences correct.

6.9 ☐ 6.5   8.47 ☐ 8.49

1 mark

Guided Question

2 Put these decimals in order starting with the **smallest**.

5.83   5.54   5.02   5.87

a) Write the numbers in place value columns. ➡

Ones	.	t	h
	.		
	.		
	.		
	.		

b) They all have the same ones digit, so look at the tenths column.

• Write the smallest number — it has the **smallest** number of tenths.   ....

• Write the next smallest number — it has the **next smallest** number of tenths.   ....

c) **The two biggest numbers have the same number of tenths. Look at their hundredths digits.**

• Write the smaller number — it's the one with **fewer** hundredths.   ....

• Write the larger number — it's the one with **more** hundredths.   ....

d) **So the correct order is:**

Smallest   **Largest**

1 mark

Ordering Decimals

3 Put these decimals in order starting with the **smallest**.

| 0.02 | 0.58 | 0.31 | 0.56 |

This is just like the last question.

Smallest   **Largest**

1 mark

4 Put these decimals in order starting with the **largest**.

| 9.7 | 9.62 | 9.04 | 9.78 |

Largest   **Smallest**

1 mark

"I can order and compare numbers with up to two decimal places."

Rounding Off

Circle all of the numbers below that are closer to 10 than to 20.

| 12 | 14 | 7 | 19 | 22 | 17 |

Circle all of the numbers below that are closer to 100 than to 200.

| 140 | 66 | 188 | 122 | 165 | 87 |

1 Round these numbers to the **nearest 10**.

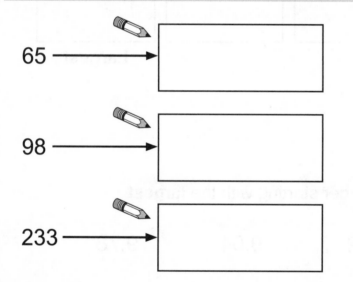

65 ⟶

98 ⟶

233 ⟶

2 marks

2 Round these numbers.

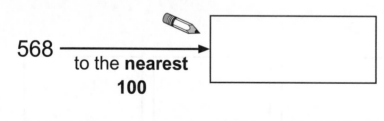

568 ⟶
to the **nearest**
100

1 mark

2450 ⟶
to the **nearest**
1000

1 mark

Rounding Off

(3) The distance from London to Rome is 1435 km.

What is this distance to the **nearest 100** km?

| km |

(4) Round 353 542:

To the **nearest 10 000**.

To the **nearest 100 000**.

(5) The weight of a blue whale was recorded as 132 650 kg.

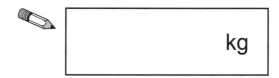

What is this weight to the **nearest 10 000** kg?

| kg |

"I can round whole numbers."

Adding and Subtracting

Warm up

Fill in the missing numbers to make these calculations correct.

5 + ... = 9   3 + ... = 7   6 + ... = 8

7 − .... = 5   10 − .... = 3   8 − .... = 4

1 **Work out these sums.**

35 + 10

1 mark

92 + 400

1 mark

2892 + 6000

1 mark

2 **Calculate:**

585 − 30

1 mark

975 − 200

1 mark

Adding and Subtracting

3) Fill in the boxes to make these calculations correct.

[   ] = 900 + 400

[   ] = 5325 − 3000

[   ] = 6165 + 3000

4) Choose **two** numbers from the list below to make the calculation correct.

2100   1800   100   400   600

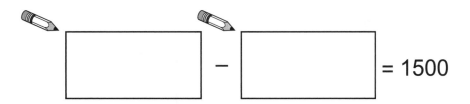

[   ] − [   ] = 1500

5) Choose **three** numbers from the list below to make the calculation correct.

1400   200   800   100   300

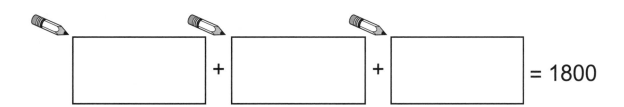

[   ] + [   ] + [   ] = 1800

"I can add and subtract multiples of 10, 100 and 1000."

Written Addition

(1) Calculate:

637 + 212

1 mark

521 + 345

1 mark

(2) Work out:

1358 + 2424

1 mark

9872 + 2213

1 mark

(3) Calculate:

8.25 + 1.13

1 mark

7.81 + 1.51

1 mark

Written Addition

 4

2456 people visited School A's summer fair.
3564 people visited School B's summer fair.

How many people visited the summer fairs in total?

 5

A clothing company buys the following numbers of coats and hats:

Coats
2295

Hats
699

How many coats and hats does the company buy in total?

1 mark

 6

A biscuit company makes 12 356 biscuits in September. They make 28 775 in October.

How many biscuits does the company make in September and October?

1 mark

"I can use standard
written methods to add."

Written Subtraction

1 Work out 7865 − 5421.

1 mark

Guided Question

2 Find the difference between 2558 and 1463.

a) Write the question like this:

- Put the bigger number on top.

- Make sure that each digit is in the right place value column.

```
    2 5 5 8
  − 1 4 6 3
  ─────────
```

b) Subtract the ones first.

```
    2 5 5 8
  − 1 4 6 3
  ─────────
        .....
```

c) Then subtract the tens, hundreds and thousands in order.

- You can't do 5 − 6 so you need to exchange 1 hundred for 10 tens.

- Then subtract the digits in the hundreds and thousands places.

```
       4  15
    2 5̶ 5̶ 8
  − 1 4 6 3
  ─────────
   ..... ..... ..... .....
```

d) Write your answer in the box.

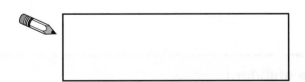

1 mark

Written Subtraction

3 Find the difference between 4668 and 2486.

This is just like the last question.

1 mark

4 Work out:

85.78 – 42.55

1 mark

24 936 – 15 443

1 mark

50.45 – 27.37

1 mark

5 A shop has 8447 tennis balls in stock.
After two months it has sold 7662 tennis balls.

How many tennis balls are left?

1 mark

"I can use standard written
methods to subtract."

Written Multiplication

(1) Work out:

23 × 3

 1 mark

35 × 7

 1 mark

(2) Calculate:

200 × 7 =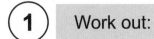

1 mark

(3) Circle the correct answer to 1604 × 5

 5126   6416   8020   9126

 1 mark

Written Multiplication

4 Calculate:

2560 × 3

1 mark

1854 × 6

1 mark

5 Calculate:

56 × 70

1 mark

486 × 30

1 mark

6 2350 people swim 30 metres each in a charity swim contest.

How many metres did they swim in total?

m

2 marks

"I can multiply a four-digit number
by a one-digit number.
I can multiply by multiples of 10."

Section Two — Calculations

Written Division

1 Calculate:

560 ÷ 4

765 ÷ 9

2 Work out:

8708 ÷ 7

9456 ÷ 6

3 Nadir earned £1152 over six months from his paper round.
He earned the same amount each month.

How much did he earn each month?

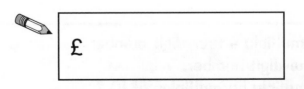

£

Written Division

4 Calculate 577 ÷ 5

Divide the numbers starting with the highest place value.

- Remember to exchange if any of the divisions aren't exact.

- If the ones don't divide exactly, write down the remainder in your answer.

$$5 \overline{)5 \ 7 \cdots 7} \quad \text{remainder} \cdots$$

remainder

1 mark

5 Calculate 2679 ÷ 6

This is just like the last question.

remainder

1 mark

6 4687 flower bulbs are put into packs of 7.

How many flower bulbs will be left over?

1 mark

"I can divide a four-digit number by a one-digit number and deal with remainders."

Multiplying and Dividing by 10, 100 and 1000

Warm up

Complete the sentences below.

To multiply by 10, the digits need to move .... place to the left.

To divide by 1000, the digits need to move .... places to the right.

To multiply by 100, the digits need to move .... places to the left.

---

(1) 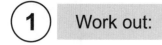 Work out:

68 × 10

1 mark

750 × 100

1 mark

15 000 ÷ 1000

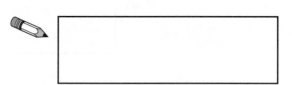

1 mark

(2) Write in the missing number for the calculations below.

16 000 ÷ [　　　] = 16

1 mark

500 ÷ [　　　] = 50

1 mark

Multiplying and Dividing by 10, 100 and 1000

3 Draw lines to match each calculation with the correct answer.

165 × 100		1.65
165 ÷ 10		1650
165 × 10		16 500
165 ÷ 100		16.5

2 marks

4 Choose the correct card to complete the calculations.

| × 10 | × 100 | × 1000 | ÷ 10 | ÷ 100 | ÷ 1000 |

62 [_____] = 6200

1 mark

0.96 = 960 [_____]

1 mark

4.57 [_____] = 4570

1 mark

"I can multiply or divide numbers by 10, 100 or 1000."

Checking Calculations

Guided Question

1 Write down a calculation to estimate 685 × 38

    a) Decide how the numbers should be rounded to make an easy calculation.

       It would be best to round 685 to the nearest 100 and 38 to the nearest 10.

       685 is ....   38 is ....
       to the nearest 100.   to the nearest 10.

    b) Write the calculation with the rounded numbers.

1 mark

2 Write a calculation to estimate the value of 912 ÷ 52

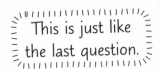

This is just like the last question.

1 mark

3 Amal calculates 58 × 7 = 406.

    Fill in the gaps below to give a calculation she could do to check her answer.

$$\boxed{} \div \boxed{} = 58$$

1 mark

Checking Calculations

 4 George calculates that 8946 ÷ 9 = 994.

Which of the following calculations could be used to check if he is correct? Circle the correct answer.

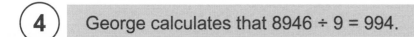 994 × 9   8946 × 994   9 × 8946

 1 mark

 5 Circle the best estimates for the following calculations:

204 + 699

 950   900   800   850

1 mark

796 − 198

750   550   600   650

 1 mark

 6 Brad calculates that 6272 − 1750 is 4572.

Check if Brad is correct using inverse operations.
Show your working.

2 marks

"I can make estimates and use inverse calculations to check my answers."

Multiples

1 Circle the numbers below that are **multiples of 5**.

55   74   56   80   90

1 mark

2 Write the **first five** multiples of 8.

1 mark

3 Write down all the multiples of 7 that are between 60 and 80.

1 mark

4 What number is missing in this sequence of multiples?

36   42   48   54   ?

1 mark

"I know how to find the
multiples of a number."

Factors

1 Circle all the **factors of 15** from the list below.

1   2   3   4   5

    6   9   10   15   30

2 Fill in the gaps to show two factor pairs of 48.

 6 × ☐ = 48   4 × ☐ = 48

3 Draw lines to join all the factor pairs of 36.

2   9

1   18

6   36

4   6

3   12

4 Eli is thinking of a number between 48 and 55.
One of its factors is 9.

What number is Eli thinking of?

"I know how to find the
factors of a number."

Prime Numbers

1 Circle **two** prime numbers from each list below:

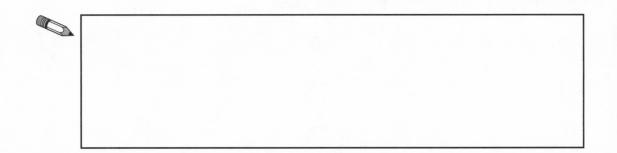

17   4   5   22   26

27   2   29   24   49

2 Is 45 a prime number? Explain your answer.

3 Find one prime number between 30 and 35.

"I know how to find prime numbers."

Square Numbers

Complete the calculations below:

4 × .... = 4^2 7 × 7 = $7^{....}$ .... × .... = 10^2

1 Calculate 3^2

1 mark

2 What is the next square number in the sequence below?

16   25   36

1 mark

3 Write down the next two square numbers after 64.

 and

2 marks

4 Work out 50^2

2 marks

"I can recognise and use square numbers."

Equivalent Fractions

Warm up

Draw a circle around all the shapes below that
have the same fraction shaded as this shape. ➜

1 Shade $\frac{1}{4}$ of each shape.

 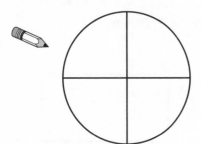   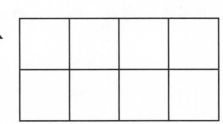

2 marks

2 Draw lines to match each shaded shape
to its equivalent fraction.

  $\frac{1}{2}$

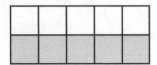 $\frac{2}{5}$

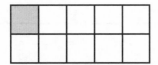 $\frac{1}{5}$

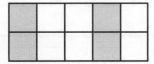 $\frac{1}{10}$

2 marks

Equivalent Fractions

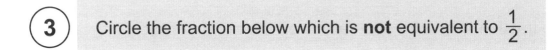

(3) Circle the fraction below which is **not** equivalent to $\frac{1}{2}$.

 $\frac{2}{4}$ $\qquad$ $\frac{6}{12}$ $\qquad$ $\frac{12}{18}$

 1 mark

(4) Draw lines to match each fraction on the top row to an equivalent fraction on the bottom row.

 $\boxed{\dfrac{1}{3}}$ $\qquad$ $\boxed{\dfrac{1}{9}}$ $\qquad$ $\boxed{\dfrac{1}{15}}$

$\boxed{\dfrac{3}{27}}$ $\qquad$ $\boxed{\dfrac{3}{9}}$ $\qquad$ $\boxed{\dfrac{2}{30}}$

2 marks

(5) Complete these equivalent fractions.

$\frac{3}{5} = \frac{\boxed{}}{10}$ $\qquad\qquad$ $\frac{4}{28} = \frac{1}{\boxed{}}$

2 marks

"I can recognise and write fractions that are equivalent to each other."

Ordering Fractions

1 Write the fraction shown by each arrow on the number line.

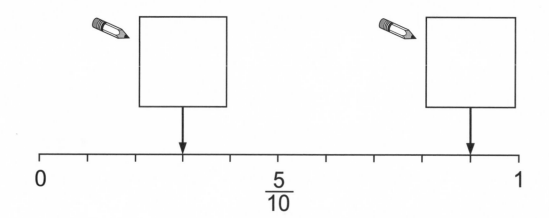

2 marks

2 Which of the fractions shown below is the **largest**?

$$\frac{8}{9} \qquad \frac{7}{9} \qquad \frac{1}{9} \qquad \frac{4}{9}$$

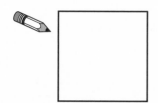

1 mark

3 Put these fractions in order, starting with the **smallest**.

$$\frac{12}{17} \qquad \frac{9}{17} \qquad \frac{15}{17} \qquad \frac{4}{17}$$

smallest   **largest**

1 mark

Ordering Fractions

Guided Question

 4 Write these fractions in order, starting with the **smallest**.

$$\frac{1}{5} \qquad \frac{7}{10} \qquad \frac{3}{20}$$

a) Find equivalent fractions so that they all have the same denominator.

- You can draw shapes to help you.

- The easiest way is to write them all with 20 as the denominator.

$$\frac{1}{5} = \frac{......}{20}$$
$$\times 4$$
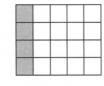

$$\frac{7}{10} = \frac{......}{20}$$
$$\times 2$$
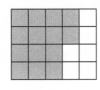

b) Compare the numerators to put these three fractions in order.

- You've got three fractions, each with 20 as the denominator.

smallest   largest

- Write them in the correct order by comparing their numerators.

$$\frac{......}{20}, \quad \frac{......}{20}, \quad \frac{......}{20}$$

c) Now write the original fractions in the correct order.

smallest   **largest**

2 marks

Ordering Fractions

5 Write these fractions in order, starting with the **smallest**.

$$\frac{2}{3} \qquad \frac{5}{6} \qquad \frac{7}{12}$$

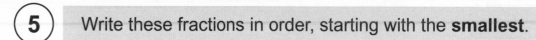

This is just like the last question.

smallest   largest

2 marks

6 Write these fractions in order, starting with the **largest**.

$$\frac{1}{2} \qquad \frac{5}{8} \qquad \frac{3}{16} \qquad \frac{9}{16}$$

largest   smallest

2 marks

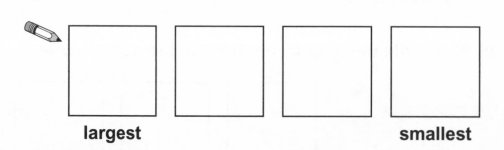

"I can compare and order fractions."

Section Three — Fractions, Decimals & Percentages   © *CGP — Not to be photocopied*

Using Fractions

(1) Find $\frac{1}{2}$ of 24.

(2) Alesha is planning a party. There are 18 guests in total.

$\frac{1}{3}$ of her guests want cake. How many guests want cake?

$\frac{1}{9}$ of her guests want jelly and ice cream.
How many guests want jelly and ice cream?

(3) Sarosh is playing basketball. He throws the ball 35 times.

$\frac{1}{5}$ of his throws go through the hoop.
How many of his throws **do not** go through the hoop?

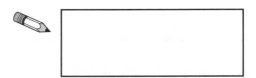

Using Fractions

4 What is $\frac{2}{3}$ of 27?

2 marks

5 50 people walked past Jermaine's school in half an hour.

$\frac{3}{5}$ of the people were wearing a coat.

How many people were wearing a coat?

2 marks

$\frac{7}{10}$ of the people were carrying a bag.

How many people were carrying a bag?

2 marks

"I can find fractions of an amount."

Section Three — Fractions, Decimals & Percentages

Adding and Subtracting Fractions

1 Find $\frac{1}{3} + \frac{1}{3}$.

1 mark

2 Find $\frac{9}{10} - \frac{8}{10}$.

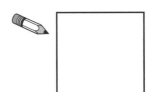

1 mark

3 Jonah and Izzy are eating a pizza together.

Jonah eats $\frac{1}{5}$ of the pizza.

Izzy eats $\frac{2}{5}$ of the pizza.

What fraction of the pizza do they eat in total?

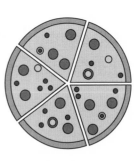

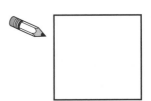

1 mark

Adding and Subtracting Fractions

(4) Find $\frac{1}{4} + \frac{1}{16}$.

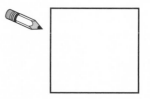

2 marks

(5) Find $\frac{8}{10} - \frac{1}{2}$.

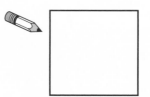

2 marks

(6) Zach and Suzy are painting a fence.

Zach paints $\frac{3}{8}$ of the fence. Suzy paints $\frac{3}{16}$ of the fence.

What fraction of the fence have they painted in total?

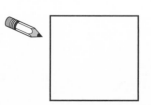

2 marks

"I can add and subtract fractions by finding equivalent fractions with the same denominator."

© CGP — NOT TO BE PHOTOCOPIED

Fractions and Decimals

Warm up

Draw a line to match each fraction to the equivalent decimal.

$\dfrac{7}{10}$ $\dfrac{1}{10}$ $\dfrac{9}{10}$ $\dfrac{3}{10}$

0.1   0.3   0.7   0.9

1   Circle the fraction that is equal to 0.65.

$\dfrac{6}{10}$ $\dfrac{5}{10}$ $\dfrac{6}{100}$ $\dfrac{65}{100}$

1 mark

2   Write $\dfrac{2}{100}$ as a decimal.

1 mark

3   Jason writes down the decimal 0.11.

What is this as a fraction?

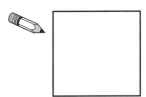

1 mark

Fractions and Decimals

 4 Write $\frac{3}{25}$ as a decimal.

a) Find an equivalent fraction that has 100 as the denominator.

- To get from 25 to 100, you multiply by 4.

- So multiply the numerator by 4 too.

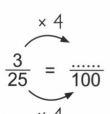

$$\frac{3}{25} = \frac{......}{100}$$

b) Now you've got a number of hundredths. So you can write it as a decimal.

2 marks

5 Write $\frac{2}{50}$ as a decimal.

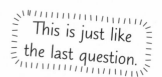 This is just like the last question.

2 marks

"I can convert between fractions and decimals."

Percentages

1 A jug is $\frac{3}{4}$ full. What is this as a percentage?

Circle the correct answer.

70% 75% 25% 34%

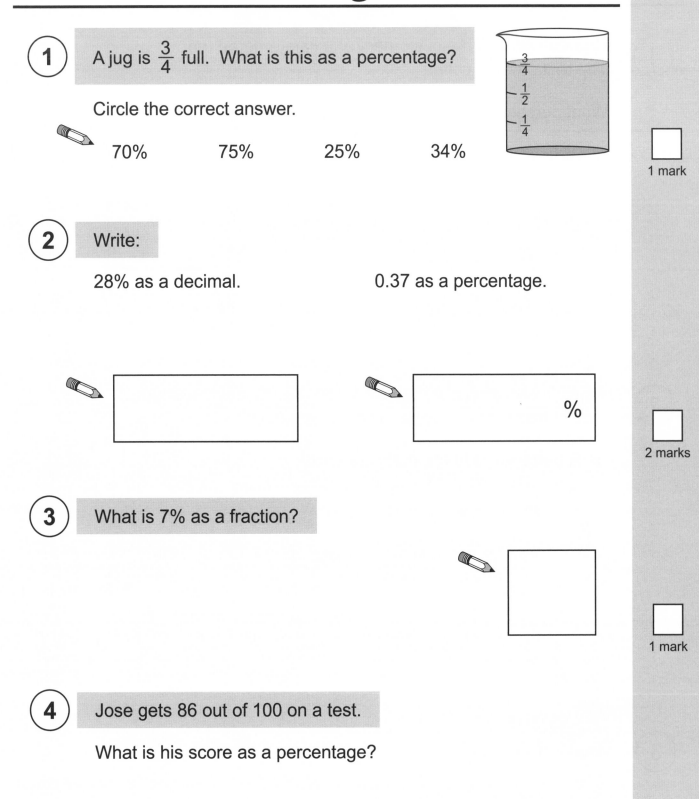

1 mark

2 Write:

28% as a decimal. 0.37 as a percentage.

%

2 marks

3 What is 7% as a fraction?

1 mark

4 Jose gets 86 out of 100 on a test.

What is his score as a percentage?

%

1 mark

"I can convert between fractions, decimals and percentages."

Percentage Problems

1 One day, 65% of the customers at a cafe ordered tea. The rest ordered coffee.

What percentage of the customers ordered coffee?

%

1 mark

2 Marco is choosing a shirt to wear. 55% of his shirts are blue. 15% of his shirts are white. The rest are pink.

What percentage of his shirts are pink?

%

1 mark

3 What is 10% of 80?

1 mark

Percentage Problems

4 There are 750 pupils in a school. 10% of them go on a trip.

How many pupils go on the trip?

1 mark

5 Alexa has 20 sweets. She gives 60% of them to her friends.

How many sweets does she give to her friends?

2 marks

6 Find 40% of 500.

2 marks

"I can find a percentage of an amount."

Section Three — Fractions, Decimals & Percentages

Section Four — Measure

Units and Conversions

---

1   Draw lines between equivalent lengths.

1 cm	100 mm
10 cm	1 m
100 cm	10 m
1000 cm	10 mm

1 mark

2   Aziz used 3 kg of flour to make some loaves of bread.

How many grams of flour did he use?

g

1 mark

Units and Conversions

3 Circle the value below which is equivalent to 3500 m.

3.5 km   0.35 km   3500 km   35 km

1 mark

4 Pete drinks 7 gallons of water in a week.

How many pints of water does he drink?
1 gallon = 8 pints

pints

1 mark

5 There are 12 inches in 1 foot.

How many feet are there in 96 inches?

feet

1 mark

How many inches are there in 6 feet 10 inches?

inches

1 mark

"I can convert between units for
measurements of length, mass and volume."

Reading Scales

1 Measure the length of the longest side of the rectangle below. Give your answer in cm.

cm

1 mark

2 What is the mass of the kettle in kilograms?

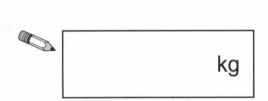

kg

1 mark

3 Alana is making cookies. She needs 125 g of butter.

Draw an arrow pointing to 125 g on this scale.

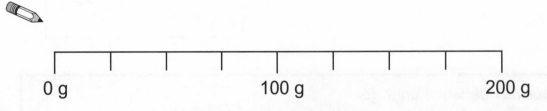

0 g   100 g   200 g

1 mark

Reading Scales

4 What is the volume of water in the jug?

ml

1 mark

5 The diagrams below show the heights of two dogs, Dog A and Dog B.

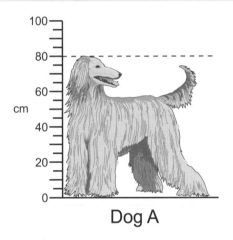

Dog A

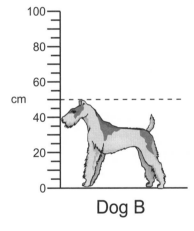

Dog B

How much taller is dog A than dog B?

cm

2 marks

"I can say what one division on a scale is worth. I can read a scale to the nearest division."

Calculating with Measures

1 The diagram below shows water in a beaker.

Leroy pours 25 ml of the water away.
How much water is left in the beaker?

ml
100
50

ml

2 Calculate the following, giving your answers in cm.

2 m + 50 cm

cm

2 cm + 80 mm

cm

3 Jean runs 2000 m every day.
How many kilometres will she run in **one week**?

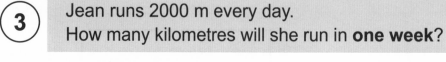

km

Calculating with Measures

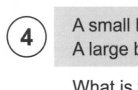

A small bag of sugar weighs 400 g.
A large bag of sugar weighs 2 kg.

What is the mass of 3 small bags and 1 large bag?
Give your answer in grams.

g

2 marks

5 A recipe for **1 jug** of fruit punch is shown on the right.

How many millilitres of apple juice are needed to make **3 jugs** of fruit punch?

Fruit Punch (1 jug)

300 ml   Orange Juice

200 ml   Apple Juice

600 ml   Lemonade

ml

1 mark

How many **litres** of lemonade are needed to make **5 jugs** of fruit punch?

litres

2 marks

"I can solve problems that involve converting between units."

Money

Draw a line to match an amount in pence with the amount in pounds.

150p		£0.15
15p		£1.50
115p		£1.15

1 Convert:

470p into pounds.

£

1 mark

£10.20 into pence.

p

1 mark

2 Natalie buys an apple for 25p and a chocolate bar for 85p.

How much does she spend in total? Give your answer in pounds.

£

1 mark

Money

3 Ciara buys a bottle of milk every day. Each bottle costs 75p.

How much does she spend on milk in 9 days?
Give your answer in pounds.

£

4 The prices of some items in a shop are shown on the right.

How much does it cost to buy one magazine and three pencils?

Price List	
Magazine	£2.30
Drink	£1.20
Pencil	55p

£

5 Moeen has £40 to spend on birthday presents for his sister. He spends £17.50 on a game and £2.10 on a card.

How much money does he have left over?

£

"I can do calculations involving money, in pounds and pence."

Section Four — Measure

Time

1 Write 9:55 pm using the 24-hour clock.

[:]

1 mark

2 The clock below shows a time early in the morning.

What time does the clock show?
Give your answer using the 24-hour clock.

[:]

1 mark

Kyle sets his alarm for 25 minutes after the time shown above.
What time does he set his alarm for?

[:]

1 mark

3 Complete these sentences.

There are [   ] days in 4 weeks.

1 mark

There are [   ] seconds in 7 minutes.

1 mark

© CGP — NOT TO BE PHOTOCOPIED

Time

Guided Question

4 Cathy leaves for a walk at 17:30 and returns home at 18:45.

How long did her walk last? Give your answer in minutes.

a) **Write the number of minutes needed to get from 17:30 to 18:00.**

17:30 $\xrightarrow{\text{+ .... minutes}}$ 18:00

b) **Write the number of minutes needed to get from 18:00 to 18:45.**

18:00 $\xrightarrow{\text{+ .... minutes}}$ 18:45

c) **Add the number of minutes together to find the total.**

minutes

1 mark

---

5 Sarah sets off to a rugby match at 12:53 and arrives at 13:48.

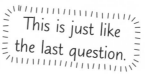
This is just like the last question.

How many minutes does it take for her to get to the match?

minutes

1 mark

Section Four — Measure

Time

6 Matthew ordered a takeaway at 19:20.
It was delivered 55 minutes later.

Show what time the takeaway was
delivered on the clock face below.

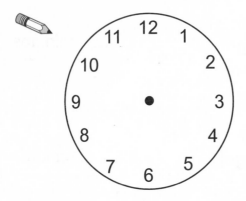

1 mark

7 Catherine watches a film that is 125 minutes long.

How long is the film in hours and minutes?

hours   minutes

1 mark

Catherine started watching the film at 18:25.
What time will it finish?

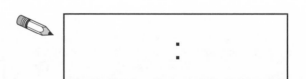

:

1 mark

"I can read, write and convert time.
I can work out how long an activity takes."

Perimeter

1 What is the perimeter of this shape?

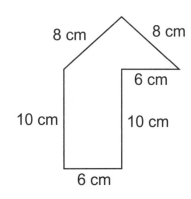

cm

2 Use a ruler to find the perimeter of this rectangle.

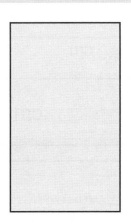

cm

3 The shape below is a regular hexagon.
Each side is 4 m long.

What is the perimeter of the regular hexagon?

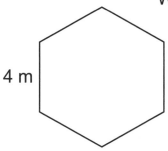

m

Section Four — Measure

Perimeter

4 Find the perimeter of this shape.

a) **Start by finding the length of the missing side.**

Look at the shape — the 8 cm side is the same length as the 5 cm side plus the missing side.

Missing side = 8 cm – 5 cm = ... cm

b) **Now, add the lengths of all the sides together to get the perimeter.**

Perimeter = 4 + 5 + 2 + 8 + 6 + ... = ... cm

cm

1 mark

5 Find the perimeter of the shape below.

This is just like the last question.

cm

1 mark

"I can find the perimeter of shapes."

Area

1) Estimate the areas of the shapes below.

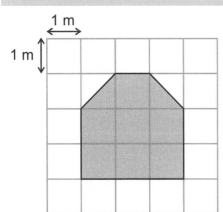

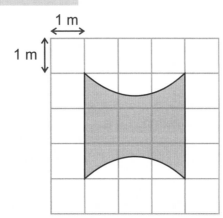

[ ] m²   [ ] m²

2 marks

2) Circle the shape which has a different area from the others.

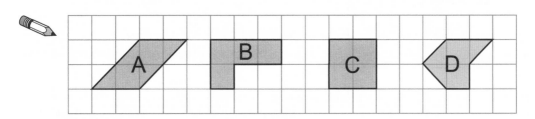

1 mark

3) Using a ruler, complete the shape below so it has an area of 7 cm².

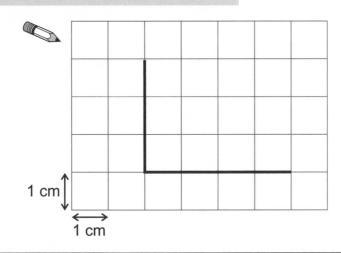

1 cm ↕
1 cm ↔

1 mark

"I can find and estimate the area of shapes."

Section Four — Measure

Areas of Squares and Rectangles

> **Warm up**
>
> Circle the correct formula for finding the area of a rectangle.
>
> Area = length ÷ width
>
> Area = length × width
>
> Area = length + width

1 What is the area of the rectangle on the grid below?

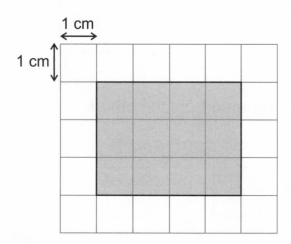

1 cm

1 cm

cm²

1 mark

2 Calculate the areas of the rectangles below.

8 cm

3 cm   A

6 mm

12 mm   B

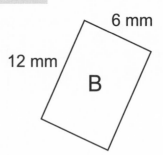

A =   cm²

B =   mm²

2 marks

Areas of Squares and Rectangles

3 Work out the area of the square below.

6 cm

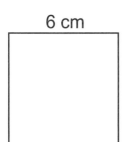

cm²

Guided Question

4 A rectangle has an area of 30 m² and a width of 5 m.

What is the length of the rectangle?

The length multiplies by the width to give 30 m².

- Put the numbers you already know into the area formula.

Length × 5 = 30

- Use inverse operations to find the length — divide 30 by 5.

Length = 30 ÷ 5 = ... m

 m

1 mark

5 A rectangle has an area of 56 m².
The length of the rectangle is 8 m.

What is the width of the rectangle?

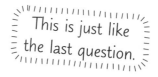 *This is just like the last question.*

m

1 mark

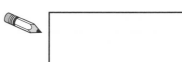

Section Four — Measure

Volume

1 Find the volume of the shapes below.

Each cube has sides of 1 cm.

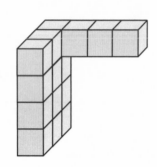
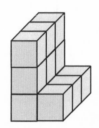

 cm³

 cm³

2 Work out volume of the cube and cuboid below.

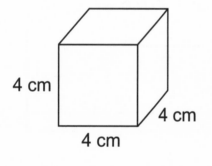

4 cm

4 cm

4 cm

 cm³

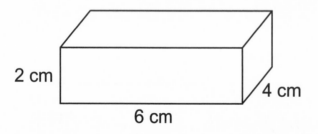

2 cm

6 cm

4 cm

 cm³

Volume

3 Circle the two cuboids that have the same volume.

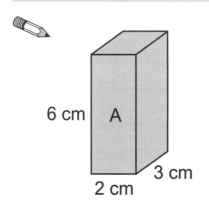

6 cm A

3 cm
2 cm

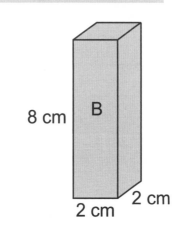

8 cm B

2 cm
2 cm

3 cm C

3 cm
3 cm

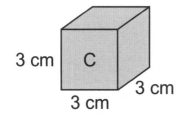

1 cm D 3 cm

12 cm

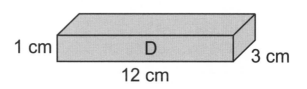

2 marks

4 Complete the table below by calculating the volume of each cuboid.

Cuboid	Length (cm)	Width (cm)	Height (cm)	Volume (cm³)
X	5	3	2	
Y	7	6	2	
Z	8	5	3	

3 marks

"I can find the volume of cubes and cuboids."

Section Five — Geometry

Measuring Angles

1 Draw lines to match each angle to its correct name.

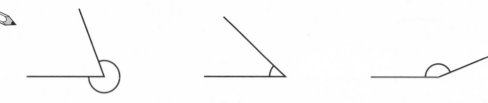

acute angle   obtuse angle   reflex angle

1 mark

2 Measure the angle below using a protractor.

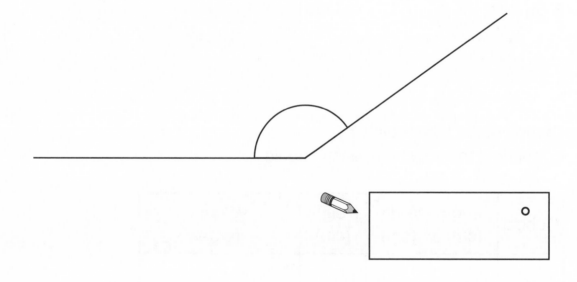

°

1 mark

3 On the line given below, use a protractor to draw a 75° angle.

1 mark

Measuring Angles

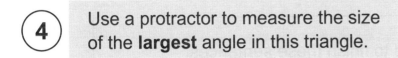

4 Use a protractor to measure the size of the **largest** angle in this triangle.

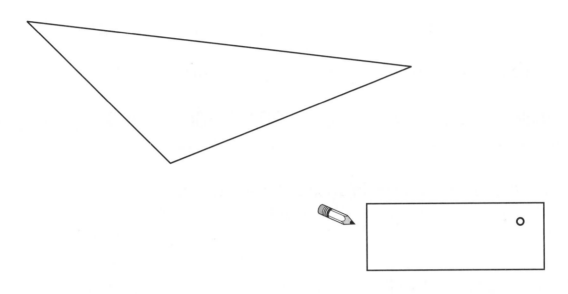

°

1 mark

5 Use a protractor to measure the size of the **acute** angle in the quadrilateral below.

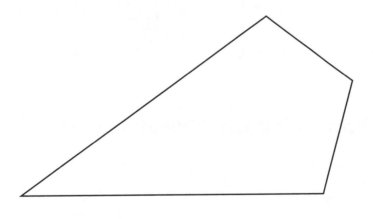

°

1 mark

"I can name, draw and measure angles."

Angles

Circle the correct angles needed to finish these sentences.

The angles on a straight line add up to   90° / 180° / 360°.

The angles around a point add up to   90° / 180° / 360°.

The angles in a right angle add up to   90° / 180° / 360°.

1 Find the missing angles in each of these right angles.

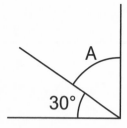

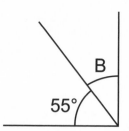

A = ☐ °

B = ☐ °

2 marks

2 Find the missing angle in each of these diagrams.

L = ☐ °

1 mark

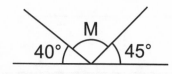

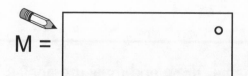

M = ☐ °

1 mark

Angles

 3 Find the missing angle in each of these diagrams.

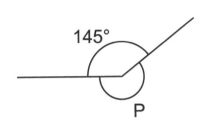

145°

P

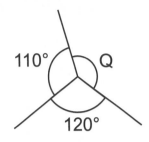

110° Q

120°

P = [   ] °

Q = [   ] °

2 marks

 4 The diagram shows a labelled angle.

Find the size of angle Y.

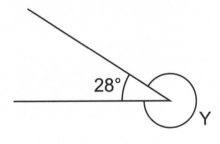

28°

Y

Y = [   ] °

1 mark

What type of angle is Y? Circle your answer.

     acute   reflex   obtuse

1 mark

"I know the sums of angles in a right angle, on a straight line and around a point."

2D Shapes

The shape on the right is a regular polygon. ⟶

Circle the shapes below which are also regular polygons.

1 Draw a line between each quadrilateral and its name.

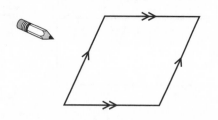

Trapezium

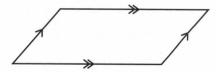

Parallelogram

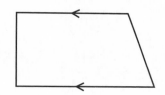

Rhombus

1 mark

2 Name the regular polygons below.

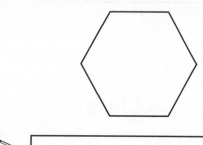

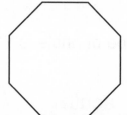

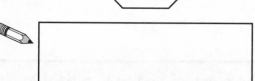

2 marks

Section Five — Geometry

© CGP — Not to be photocopied

2D Shapes

3 Match each type of triangle with its description.

It has 3 equal angles
and 3 equal sides.

Isosceles

All sides and
angles are different.

Equilateral

It has 2 equal sides
and 2 equal angles.

Scalene

1 mark

4 Two sides of a kite have been drawn on the grid below.

Use a ruler to complete the kite.

1 mark

"I know the properties of different shapes."

3D Shapes

Warm up

Circle all the 3D shapes from the words below.

Square   Rhombus   Cylinder

Prism   Triangle   Cuboid

(1) Write down the name of each 3D shape below.

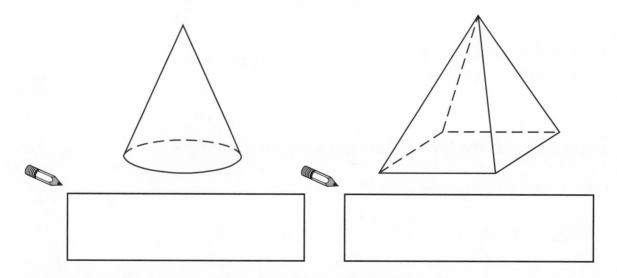

2 marks

(2) Name the 3D shapes being described below.

It is a prism where both end faces are circles.

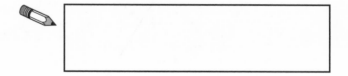

1 mark

It has 6 rectangular faces, 8 vertices and 12 edges.

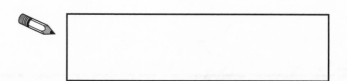

1 mark

3D Shapes

3 Circle the net that could be used to make a triangular prism.

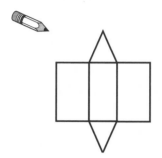 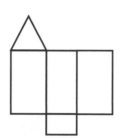 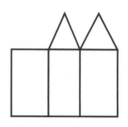

1 mark

4 Which of these nets could **not** be used to make a cuboid?

Circle the correct answer.

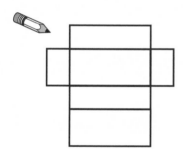 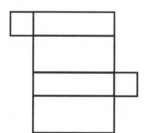 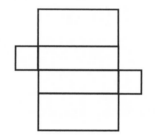

1 mark

5 Here is the net of a cube.

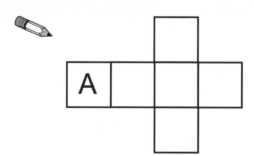

Shade the face that will be **opposite**
face A when the net is folded into a cube.

1 mark

"I can recognise and describe
3D shapes and their nets."

Section Five — Geometry

Coordinates

1 What are the coordinates of the points plotted below?

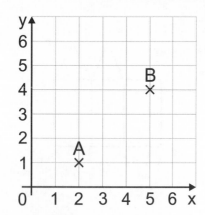

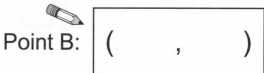

Point A: (,   )

Point B: (,   )

1 mark

2 Plot points F, G and H on the grid on the right.

F (5, 3)

G (7, 2)

H (4, 7)

1 mark

3 Find the coordinates of the points plotted on the grid below.

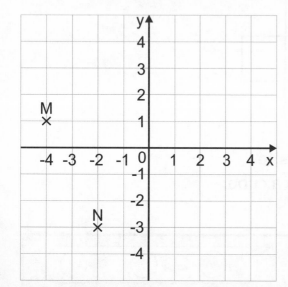

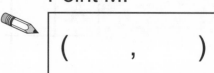

Point M:

(,   )

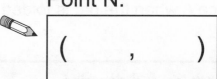

Point N:

(,   )

1 mark

Coordinates

4 Plot points P, Q, R and S on the grid below.

P (3, 2)

Q (–1, –3)

R (–1, 2)

S (4, –3)

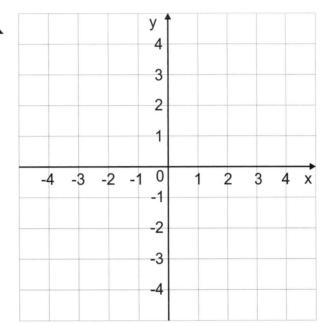

1 mark

5 Three corners of a rectangle are marked on the grid below.

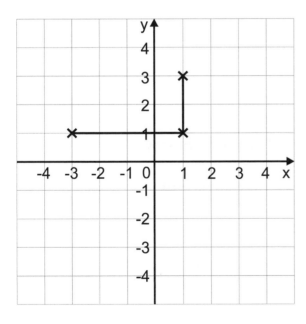

Find the coordinates of the point marking the missing corner of the rectangle.

(,   )

1 mark

"I can use coordinates in four quadrants."

Reflection

1 Reflect shape A in the mirror line.

Label the reflected shape B.

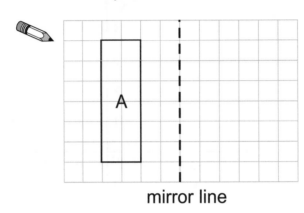

mirror line

2 Reflect shape C in the mirror line.

Label the reflected shape D.

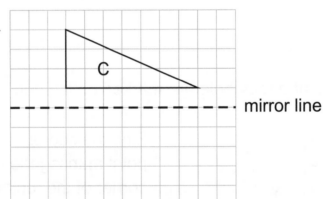

mirror line

3 A shape is shown inside a border of squares below.

Draw the reflection of the shape in the mirror line.

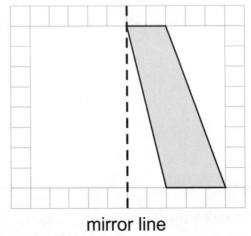

mirror line

Reflection

Guided Question

4 Reflect shape G in the y-axis.
Label the reflected shape H.

a) **For each corner of shape G, count how many squares it is to the left of the y-axis.**

- The y-axis is the vertical axis.

- The bottom left corner of shape G is 5 squares from the y-axis.

- Count how many squares the other two corners are from the y-axis.

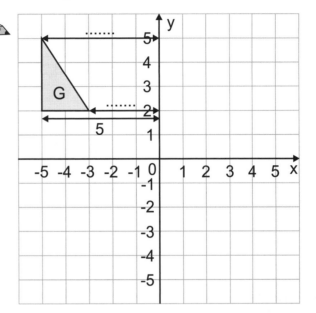

b) **Count the same number of squares to the right of the y-axis to draw the corners of the reflected shape.**

- Count the same number of squares to the right of the y-axis.

- Mark each corner of the reflected shape with a cross.

- Join up the crosses and label the shape, H.

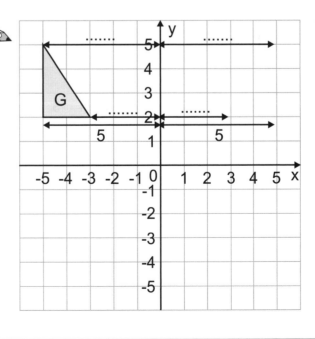

1 mark

Section Five — Geometry

Reflection

5 Shape J is shown on the grid below.

This is just like the last question.

Reflect shape J in the y-axis.

Label the reflected shape K.

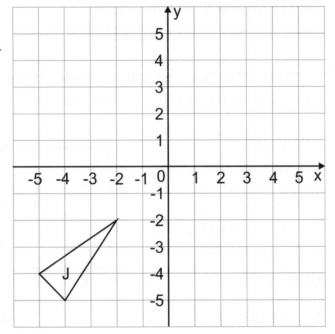

6 Shape P is shown on the grid below.

Reflect the shape P in the x-axis.

Label the reflected shape Q.

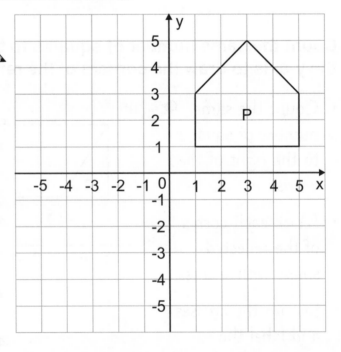

"I can reflect shapes in a mirror line and in the x- and y- axes."

Translation

Warm up

Circle the example below which shows
a translation from shape A to shape B.

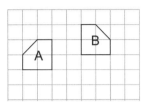 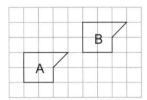 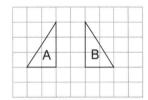

1 Translate triangle A 3 squares to the left and 2 squares down.

Label the new triangle B.

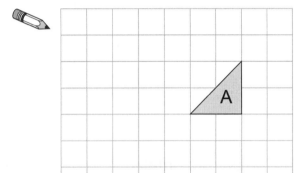

1 mark

2 Translate shape C 3 squares to the right and 4 squares up.

Label the new shape D.

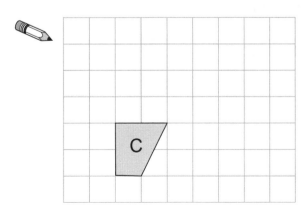

1 mark

Section Five — Geometry

Translation

(3) Translate shape E –6 units horizontally and –5 units vertically on the grid below.

**–6 units horizontally means 6 units left and
–5 units vertically means 5 units down.**

- Translate each corner of shape E 6 units left and 5 units down. Mark each translated corner with a cross.

- Join up the crosses to make the translated shape.

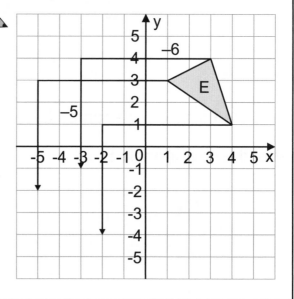

1 mark

(4) Translate shape G +7 units horizontally and –4 units vertically on the grid below.

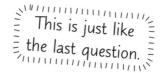
This is just like the last question.

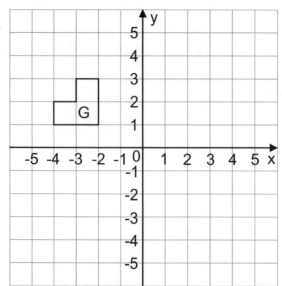

1 mark

"I can translate shapes on a grid."

Tables

Warm up

Cormac sells crisps at the tuck shop.

One day he sold 12 bags of salt and vinegar crisps,
15 bags of beef crisps and 35 bags of ready salted crisps.

Put this data into the table below.

Flavour	Ready Salted	Salt and Vinegar	Beef
Number of bags sold	....	....	....

---

1 The table below shows how the children in Year 5 travel to school.

Travel method	Number of pupils
Car	1
Bus	10
Walk	21
Bike	15
Train	3

How many children ride a bike to school?

1 mark

What is the total number of children who travel by car, bus or train?

1 mark

Tables

2 The table shows the number of cakes a shop sold on five days.

Day	Monday	Tuesday	Wednesday	Thursday	Friday
Number of cakes	52	39	37	45	23

How many **more** cakes were sold on Monday than on Friday?

1 mark

Guided Question

3 Here is the morning bus timetable from Brouton to Millum.

Brouton	7:35	7:50	8:10	8:35
Rexhill	7:45	8:00	8:20	8:45
Durby	8:03	8:18	8:38	9:03
Chadham	8:10	8:25	8:45	9:10
Millum	8:22	8:37	8:57	9:22

Mark needs to be in Millum by 9:00 am.
What is the latest bus he can catch from Rexhill?

a) On the Millum row of the timetable, find the last time before 9:00 am.

This is the bus Mark needs to arrive on. .... am

b) Go straight up from this time until you reach the Rexhill row.

This is the latest time he can catch a bus from Rexhill.

am

1 mark

Tables

 4 The timetable below shows train times for the journey between Ashdown and Park Grove

Ashdown	12:40	13:00	13:20	14:00
Hillgate	13:05	13:25	14:05	14:25
Stanton	13:25	13:45	14:25	14:45
Stow on Rye	14:00	14:20	15:00	15:20
Park Grove	14:15	14:35	15:15	15:35

Shawama needs to be in Stow on Rye by 15:10.
What's the latest train she can catch from Ashdown?

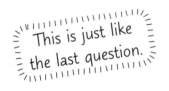
This is just like the last question.

1 mark

Fraser catches the 14:25 train from Hillgate.
What time will he arrive in Park Grove?

1 mark

Rhian gets the 12:40 train from Ashdown to Stanton.
How long did her journey take?

minutes

1 mark

"I can read and use information in tables and timetables."

Pictograms and Bar Charts

1 The bar chart shows the eye colours of a group of children.

6 children had blue eyes. 3 children had green eyes.

Complete the bar chart to show this.

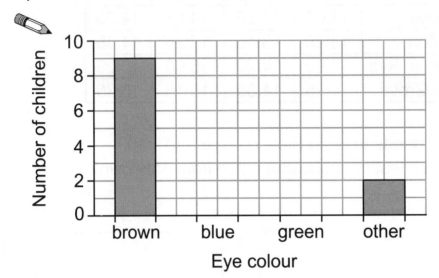

2 This pictogram shows how many pieces of fruit David ate over a weekend.

David			
Isobel			

$\square$ = 2 pieces of fruit

Isobel ate 9 pieces of fruit.
Complete the pictogram to show this.

How many more pieces of fruit did Isobel eat than David?

Pictograms and Bar Charts

3 The bar chart below shows how many burgers, hotdogs, wraps and salads were sold at a barbecue.

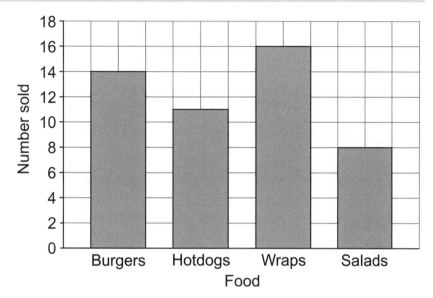

How many hotdogs and salads were sold in total?

4 The pictogram below shows how many dogs, cats and fish there are in a pet shop.

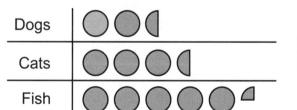

How many dogs, cats and fish are in the pet shop in total?

"I can solve problems using data from pictograms and bar charts."

Line Graphs

1 Sarah's height has been measured each year.

The line graph below shows how her height has changed.

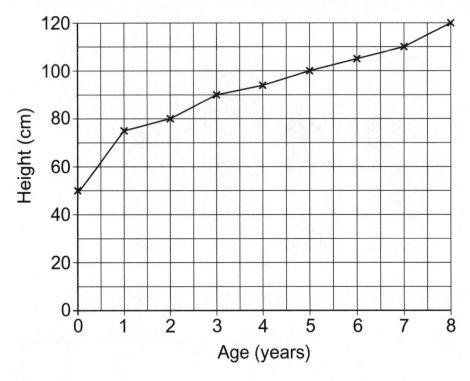

How tall was Sarah when she was 2 years old?

cm

1 mark

How old was Sarah when she was 100 cm tall?

1 mark

How many centimetres did Sarah grow
between the ages of 3 and 7?

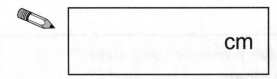

cm

2 marks

Line Graphs

(2) The line graph shows how the population of two villages, Teignton and Cragston, changed between 1995 and 2015.

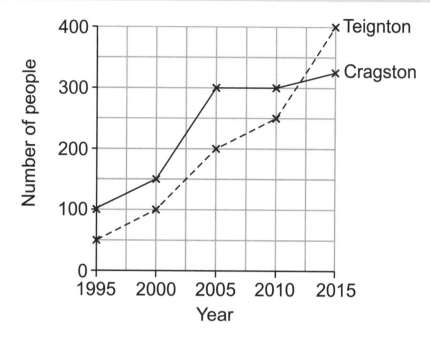

What was the population of Cragston in 2000?

One year, Cragston had a population of 300 and Teignton had a population of 200. What year was this?

In 2010, how many people lived in Cragston and Teignton in total?

"I can present data and solve problems using line graphs."

Practice Test 2

1 Calculate 672 − 30

1 mark

2 Work out the area of this rectangle.

8 cm

5 cm

cm²

1 mark

3 Work out 9².

1 mark

4 Complete these conversions.

7 cm = ⬚ mm

1 mark

8000 ml = ⬚ litres

1 mark

5 Write the Roman numeral CCXV in numbers.

1 mark

6 Draw the reflection of shape X in the mirror line.

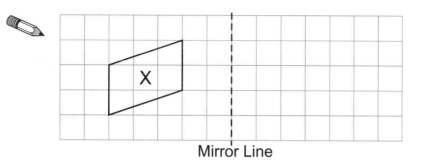

Mirror Line

7 Write the missing values to make these equivalent fractions correct.

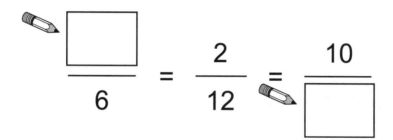

$$\frac{}{6} = \frac{2}{12} = \frac{10}{}$$

8 Calculate 1273 × 6

9 Put these decimals in order starting with the **smallest**.

2.78   2.09   2.46   2.49

Smallest			**Largest**

Practice Test 2

10 Lemons cost 35p each and pineapples cost £1.35 each.

How which will it cost to buy
3 lemons and a pineapple?

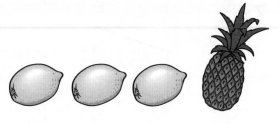

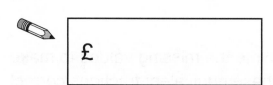

£

2 marks

11 Work out the **perimeter** of the shape below.

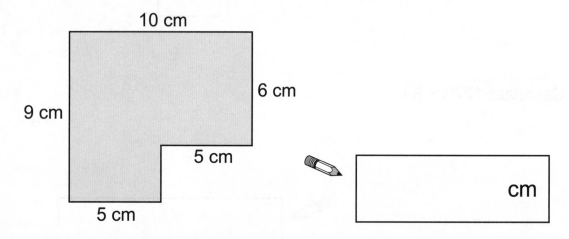

10 cm

6 cm

9 cm

5 cm

5 cm

cm

2 marks

12 Some of the circle below has been shaded.

What percentage of the circle is shaded?

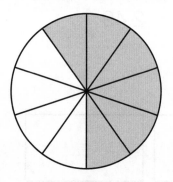

%

1 mark

13 An irregular quadrilateral is shown below.

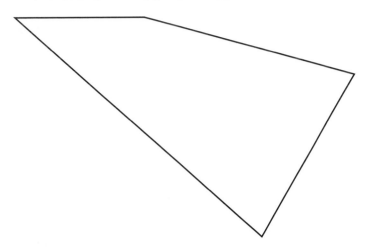

Use a protractor to measure the angle of the **obtuse angle**.

°

1 mark

Use a ruler to measure the length of the **shortest side** in millimetres.

mm

1 mark

14 A bus timetable is shown below.

Lawes	13:00	13:20	13:40	14:00
Launchbury	13:14	13:34	13:52	14:14
East Wood	13:29	13:49	14:07	14:29
Attwood	13:47	14:07	14:25	14:47
Castle Ford	13:54	14:14	14:32	14:54

Nigel gets the 13:40 bus from Lawes to Attwood.
How long does his journey take?

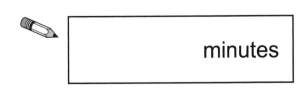

minutes

2 marks

Total

Practice Test 2

Answers

Pages 2-5 — Practice Test 1

Q1 **5** *(1 mark)*

2 *(1 mark)*

Q2 The shape is divided into 10 squares. $\frac{2}{5} = \frac{4}{10}$ so you need to shade 4 squares.

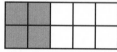

(1 mark for any four squares shaded.)

Q3
```
  7 6 2 1
+ 1 2 9 0
─────────
  8 9 1 1  (1 mark)
  1
```

Q4 **11** *(1 mark)*

Q5 Trifles sold = 11
Ice Creams sold = 2
So 11 − 2 = **9** more trifles were sold.
(2 marks for the correct answer. Otherwise 1 mark for finding the number of trifles and ice creams.)

Q6 Count on 8 places from −6:
−6 + 8 = **2** *(1 mark)*

Count back 11 places from 6:
6 − 11 = **−5** *(1 mark)*

Q7

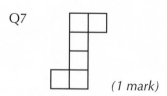

(1 mark)

Q8 All the numbers have the same digit in the ten thousands place so look at the digits in the thousands places: 4 < 6 < 8
So the correct order is:
84 100, 86 400, 88 300
(1 mark)

Q9 When rounding 820 to the nearest 100 the decider is the tens digit, which is 2, so round down to **800**. *(1 mark)*

When rounding 62 820 to the nearest 1000 the decider is the hundreds digit, which is 8, so round up to **63 000**. *(1 mark)*

Q10

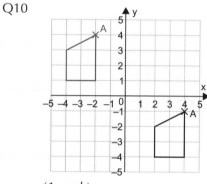

(1 mark)

(4, −1) *(1 mark)*

Q11 Angles around a point add up to 360°.
So Angle m = 360° − 110°
　　　　　　= **250°** *(1 mark)*

Q12
```
    0 1 8 8  remainder 2
6 ) 1 ¹1 ⁵3 ⁵0
```
There will be **188** sticks in each campfire. *(1 mark)*

There will be **2** sticks left over. *(1 mark)*

Q13 10% of 60 = 60 ÷ 10 = 6
30% of 60 = 3 × 6 = **18**
(2 marks for the correct a answer. Otherwise 1 mark for finding 10% of 60.)

Section One — Number & Place Value

Pages 6-7 — Place Value

Q1 **7** *(1 mark)*

0 *(1 mark)*

Q2 **400** *(1 mark)*

20 000 *(1 mark)*

Q3 **8046** *(1 mark)*

Q4 **Nine thousand, two hundred and ten** *(1 mark)*

Q5 **8972, 128 547, 38 083** *(1 mark)*

Q6 **123 815** *(1 mark)*

Q7 **Two hundred and ten thousand, two hundred and sixty three** *(1 mark)*

Pages 8-9 — Ordering Numbers

Q1 **246** *(1 mark)*

Q2 **6322** *(1 mark)*

Q3 923 < 955 and 5280 > 5264 *(1 mark for both correct)*

Q4 **8260, 8210, 8120** *(1 mark)*

Q5 **£88 900, £90 600, £96 200, £99 300** *(1 mark)*

Q6 **268 900, 260 600, 232 200, 222 300** *(1 mark)*

Answers

Pages 10-11 —
Negative Numbers

Q1 Count on 3 places from –5:
–5 + 3 = **–2** *(1 mark)*

Count back 7 places from –2:
–2 – 7 = **–9** *(1 mark)*

Q2 Count on 4 places from –2:
–2 + 4 = **2** *(1 mark)*

Count back 8 places from 5:
5 – 8 = **–3** *(1 mark)*

Q3 Count on 9 places from –8:
–8 + 9 = **1** *(1 mark)*

Count back 10 places from 3:
3 – 10 = **–7** *(1 mark)*

Q4 Count on 6 places from –3.
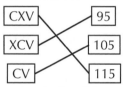
–3 + 6 = 3
So the missing number is **3**.
(1 mark)

Q5 Count on 5 places from –1:
–1 + 5 = 4
So the missing number is **4**.
(1 mark)

Count back 8 places from 2:
2 – 8 = –6
So the missing number is **–6**.
(1 mark)

Page 12 —
Roman Numerals

Warm up
I = **1**, V = **5**, X = **10**,
L = **50**, C = **100**

Q1 XVI = 10 + 5 + 1 = **16**
(1 mark)

LXXV = 50 + 10 + 10 + 5
= **75** *(1 mark)*

Q2 XC has a small letter before a big one so subtract.
XC = 100 – 10 = 90
XL has a small letter before a big one so subtract.
XL = 50 – 10 = 40
CVI = 100 + 5 + 1 = 106
XXIV has a small letter before a big one (IV) so subtract first.
IV = 5 – 1 = 4 so
XXIV = 10 + 10 + 4 = 24
XL and **XXIV** are less than 50.
(2 marks for both correct numerals circled. Otherwise 1 mark if only one correct numeral is circled.)

Q3 CXV = 100 + 10 + 5 = 115
XCV has a small letter before a big one (XC) so subtract first.
XC = 100 – 10 = 90
XCV = 90 + 5 = 95
CV = 100 + 5 = 105

CXV		95
XCV		105
CV		115

(2 marks for all lines correct. Otherwise 1 mark for one correct line.)

Page 13 — Decimals

Q1 **3** *(1 mark)*

7 *(1 mark)*

Q2 **0.05** *(1 mark)*

Q3 The first number line is split into tenths. The first arrow is 2 tenths more than 0 so it's pointing to **0.2**
The second arrow is 1 tenth less than 1 so it's pointing to **0.9**
(1 mark for both values correct.)

The second number line is split into hundredths. The first arrow is 3 hundredths more than 0.6 so it's pointing to **0.63**
The second arrow is 2 hundredths less than 0.7 so it's pointing to **0.68**
(1 mark for both values correct.)

Pages 14-15 —
Ordering Decimals

Q1 6.9 > 6.5 and 8.47 < 8.49
(1 mark for both correct)

Q2 Write the numbers in place value columns.

Ones	.	t	h
5	.	8	3
5	.	5	4
5	.	0	2
5	.	8	7

They all have the same ones digit, so look at the tenths column.
5.02 has 0 tenths so it's the smallest.
5.54 has 5 tenths so it's the next smallest.
The other two numbers have 8 tenths so look at their hundredths digits.
5.83 has 3 hundredths.
5.87 has 7 hundredths.
So 5.83 is smaller than 5.87.
The correct order is:
5.02, 5.54, 5.83, 5.87
(1 mark)

Q3 **0.02, 0.31, 0.56, 0.58**
(1 mark)

Q4 **9.78, 9.7, 9.62, 9.04**
(1 mark)

Answers

Pages 16-17 —
Rounding Off

Warm up

The numbers that are closer to 10 than 20 are: **7, 12, 14**

The numbers that are closer to 100 than 200 are: **140, 66, 122, 87**

Q1 When rounding to the nearest 10 the decider is in the ones place.
For 65 the decider is 5 so round up to **70**.
For 98 the decider is 8 so round up to **100**.
For 233 the decider is 3 so round down to **230**.
(2 marks for all three correct. Otherwise 1 mark for any two correct.)

Q2 When rounding 568 to the nearest 100 the decider is 6 so round up to **600**. *(1 mark)*

When rounding 2450 to the nearest 1000 the decider is 4 so round down to **2000**. *(1 mark)*

Q3 When rounding 1435 km to the nearest 100 km the decider is 3 so round down to **1400 km**. *(1 mark)*

Q4 When rounding 353 542 to the nearest 10 000 the decider is 3 so round down to **350 000**. *(1 mark)*

When rounding 353 542 to the nearest 100 000 the decider is 5 so round up to **400 000**. *(1 mark)*

Q5 When rounding 132 650 kg to the nearest 10 000 kg the decider is 2 so round down to **130 000 kg**. *(1 mark)*

Section Two —
Calculations

Pages 18-19 —
Adding and Subtracting

Warm up
$5 + 4 = 9$
$3 + 4 = 7$
$6 + 2 = 8$
$7 - 2 = 5$
$10 - 7 = 3$
$8 - 4 = 4$

Q1 $35 + 10 = \mathbf{45}$ *(1 mark)*

$92 + 400 = \mathbf{492}$ *(1 mark)*

$2892 + 6000 = \mathbf{8892}$ *(1 mark)*

Q2 $585 - 30 = \mathbf{555}$ *(1 mark)*

$975 - 200 = \mathbf{775}$ *(1 mark)*

Q3 $\mathbf{1300} = 900 + 400$ *(1 mark)*

$\mathbf{2325} = 5325 - 3000$ *(1 mark)*

$\mathbf{9165} = 6165 + 3000$ *(1 mark)*

Q4 $\mathbf{2100} - \mathbf{600} = 1500$ *(1 mark)*

Q5 $\mathbf{1400} + \mathbf{300} + \mathbf{100} = 1800$ *(1 mark)*

Pages 20-21 —
Written Addition

Q1
```
   6 3 7
 + 2 1 2
   8 4 9   (1 mark)
```

```
   5 2 1
 + 3 4 5
   8 6 6   (1 mark)
```

Q2
```
   1 3 5 8
 + 2 4 2 4
   3 7 8 2   (1 mark)
       1
```

```
     9 8 7 2
 +   2 2 1 3
   1 2 0 8 5   (1 mark)
     1   1
```

Q3
```
   8 . 2 5
 + 1 . 1 3
   9 . 3 8   (1 mark)
```

```
   7 . 8 1
 + 1 . 5 1
   9 . 3 2   (1 mark)
       1
```

Q4
```
   2 4 5 6
 + 3 5 6 4
   6 0 2 0
   1 1 1
```
So **6020** people visited the fairs. *(1 mark)*

Q5
```
   2 2 9 5
 +   6 9 9
   2 9 9 4
     1 1
```
So the company bought **2994** coats and hats. *(1 mark)*

Q6
```
   1 2 3 5 6
 + 2 8 7 7 5
   4 1 1 3 1
   1 1 1 1
```
So the company makes **41 131** biscuits in September and October. *(1 mark)*

Answers

Pages 22-23 —
Written Subtraction

Q1
```
   7 8 6 5
 − 5 4 2 1
   ‾‾‾‾‾‾‾
   2 4 4 4
```
(1 mark)

Q2
```
     4 15
   2 5̸ 5̸ 8
 − 1 4 6 3
   ‾‾‾‾‾‾‾
   1 0 9 5
```
(1 mark)

Q3
```
     5 16
   4 6̸ 6̸ 8
 − 2 4 8 6
   ‾‾‾‾‾‾‾
   2 1 8 2
```
(1 mark)

Q4
```
   8 5 . 7 8
 − 4 2 . 5 5
   ‾‾‾‾‾‾‾‾‾
   4 3 . 2 3
```
(1 mark)

```
   1 14 8 13
   2̸ 4̸ 9̸ 3̸ 6
 −   1 5 4 4 3
     ‾‾‾‾‾‾‾‾‾
       9 4 9 3
```
(1 mark)

```
   4 10   3 15
   3̸ 0̸ . 4̸ 3̸
 − 2 7 . 3 7
   ‾‾‾‾‾‾‾‾‾
   2 3 . 0 8
```
(1 mark)

Q5
```
   7 13  14
   8̸ 4̸ 4̸ 7
 − 7 6 6 2
   ‾‾‾‾‾‾‾
     7 8 5
```
So **785** tennis balls are left.
(1 mark)

Pages 24-25 —
Written Multiplication

Warm up
$5 × \mathbf{4} = 20$
$7 × 6 = \mathbf{42}$

Q1
```
     2 3
   ×   3
   ‾‾‾‾‾
     6 9
```
(1 mark)

```
     3 5
   ×   7
   ‾‾‾‾‾
   2 4 5
     2 3
```
(1 mark)

Q2
```
   2 0 0
 ×     7
 ‾‾‾‾‾‾‾
 1 4 0 0
     1
```
(1 mark)

Q3
```
   1 6 0 4
 ×       5
 ‾‾‾‾‾‾‾‾‾
 8 0 2 0
   3   2
```
(1 mark)

Q4
```
   2 5 6 0
 ×       3
 ‾‾‾‾‾‾‾‾‾
 7 6 8 0
   1 1
```
(1 mark)

```
   1 8 5 4
 ×       6
 ‾‾‾‾‾‾‾‾‾
 1 1 1 2 4
   1 5 3 2
```
(1 mark)

Q5
$56 × 70 = 56 × 7 × 10$
Start by multiplying 56 by 7:
```
     5 6
   ×   7
   ‾‾‾‾‾
   3 9 2
   3 4
```
Then multiply your answer
by 10: $392 × 10 = \mathbf{3920}$
(1 mark)

$486 × 30 = 486 × 3 × 10$
Start by multiplying 486 by 3:
```
     4 8 6
   ×     3
   ‾‾‾‾‾‾‾
   1 4 5 8
   1 2 1
```
Then multiply your answer by
10: $1458 × 10 = \mathbf{14\,580}$
(1 mark)

Q6
$2350 × 30 = 2350 × 3 × 10$
Start by multiplying 2350
by 3:
```
   2 3 5 0
 ×       3
 ‾‾‾‾‾‾‾‾‾
 7 0 5 0
   1 1
```
Then multiply your answer by
10: $7050 × 10 = \mathbf{70\,500\ m}$
*(2 marks for the correct
answer. Otherwise 1 mark
for correct working.)*

Answers

Pages 26-27 — Written Division

Q1

$$4 \overline{\smash{)}5\,^16\,0} \quad 1\,4\,0$$ *(1 mark)*

$$9 \overline{\smash{)}7\,^76\,^45} \quad 0\,8\,5$$ *(1 mark)*

Q2

$$7 \overline{\smash{)}8\,^17\,^30\,^28} \quad 1\,2\,4\,4$$ *(1 mark)*

$$6 \overline{\smash{)}9\,^34\,^45\,^36} \quad 1\,5\,7\,6$$ *(1 mark)*

Q3

$$6 \overline{\smash{)}1\,^11\,^55\,^12} \quad 0\,1\,9\,2$$

Each month he earned **£192**. *(1 mark)*.

Q4

$$5 \overline{\smash{)}5\,7\,^27} \quad 1\,1\,5 \text{ remainder } 2$$

115 remainder **2** *(1 mark)*

Q5

$$6 \overline{\smash{)}2\,^26\,^27\,^39} \quad 0\,4\,4\,6 \text{ remainder } 3$$

446 remainder **3** *(1 mark)*

Q6

$$7 \overline{\smash{)}4\,^46\,^48\,^67} \quad 0\,6\,6\,9 \text{ remainder } 4$$

There will be **4** flower bulbs left over. *(1 mark)*

Pages 28-29 — Multiplying and Dividing by 10, 100 and 1000

Warm Up

To multiply by 10, the digits need to move **one** place to the left.
To divide by 1000, the digits need to move **three** places to the right.
To multiply by 100, the digits need to move **two** places to the left.

Q1 68 × 10 = **680** *(1 mark)*

750 × 100 = **75 000** *(1 mark)*

15 000 ÷ 1000 = **15** *(1 mark)*

Q2 16 000 ÷ **1000** = 16 *(1 mark)*

500 ÷ **10** = 50 *(1 mark)*

Q3

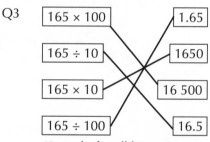

(2 marks for all lines correct. Otherwise 1 mark for at least two lines correct.)

Q4 62 × **100** = 6200 *(1 mark)*

0.96 = 960 ÷ **1000** *(1 mark)*

4.57 × **1000** = 4570 *(1 mark)*

Pages 30-31 — Checking Calculations

Q1 685 is 700 to the nearest 100.
38 is 40 to the nearest 10.
So a good estimate of the calculation would be:
700 × 40 *(1 mark)*

Q2 912 is 900 to the nearest 100.
52 is 50 to the nearest 10.
So a good estimate of the calculation would be:
900 ÷ 50 *(1 mark)*

Q3 **406 ÷ 7** = 58 *(1 mark)*

Q4 **994 × 9** *(1 mark)*

Q5 Rounding each number to the nearest 100 gives:
200 + 700 = **900** *(1 mark)*

Rounding each number to the nearest 100 gives:
800 − 200 = **600** *(1 mark)*

Q6 Brad should do 4572 + 1750 and see if he gets 6272.

$$\begin{array}{r} 4\,5\,7\,2 \\ +\,1\,7\,5\,0 \\ \hline 6\,3\,2\,2 \\ {\scriptstyle 1\ 1} \end{array}$$

So Brad is **incorrect**.
(1 mark for the correct answer and 1 mark for the correct explanation.)

Answers

Page 32 — Multiples

Q1 **55**, **80**, **90** *(1 mark)*

Q2 **8**, **16**, **24**, **32**, **40** *(1 mark)*

Q3 **63**, **70**, **77** *(1 mark)*

Q4 42 − 36 = 6
The sequence is multiples of 6, so the missing number will be 54 + 6 = **60** *(1 mark)*

Page 33 — Factors

Q1 **1**, **3**, **5**, **15** *(1 mark)*

Q2 6 × **8** = 48 *(1 mark)*
4 × **12** = 48 *(1 mark)*

Q3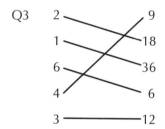
(2 marks for all pairs joined correctly. Otherwise 1 mark for at least two pairs joined correctly.)

Q4 **54** *(1 mark)*

Page 34 — Prime Numbers

Q1 **17** and **5**
(1 mark for both correct.)

2 and **29**
(1 mark for both correct.)

Q2 45 is **not** a prime number. It has factors other than 1 and 45 (the other factors are 3, 5, 9 and 15).
(1 mark for saying that 45 is not a prime number, 1 mark for a correct explanation.)

Q3 31 and 33 could be prime numbers as they end with a 1 or a 3.
33 ÷ 3 = 11, so 33 has factors other than 1 and 33 so it isn't prime. 31 has no other factors other than itself and 1, so **31** is the only prime number between 30 and 35.
(1 mark)

Page 35 — Square Numbers

Warm up
4 × **4** = 4²
7 × 7 = 7²
10 × 10 = 10²

Q1 3² = 3 × 3 = **9** *(1 mark)*

Q2 The sequence is square numbers. 16 = 4 × 4, 25 = 5 × 5 and 36 = 6 × 6 so the next square number will be 7 × 7 = **49** *(1 mark)*

Q3 64 = 8 × 8
so 9 × 9 = **81** *(1 mark)*
and 10 × 10 = **100** *(1 mark)*

Q4 50² = 50 × 50
= 5 × 10 × 5 × 10
= 5 × 5 × 10 × 10
= 25 × 100
= **2500**
(2 marks for the correct answer. Otherwise 1 mark for correct working.)

Section Three — Fractions, Decimals & Percentages

Pages 36-37 — Equivalent Fractions

Warm up
The shape has $\frac{1}{3}$ shaded.
The other shapes that have $\frac{1}{3}$ shaded are:

Q1 In the first shape, 1 sector should be shaded. E.g.
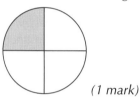
(1 mark)

In the second shape, 2 squares should be shaded. E.g.
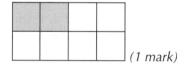
(1 mark)

Q2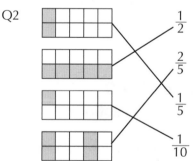
(2 marks for matching all four correctly. Otherwise 1 mark for matching two pairs correctly.)

Answers

Q3

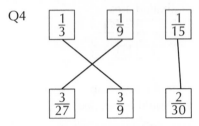

$$\frac{1}{2} = \frac{2}{4} \quad \frac{1}{2} = \frac{6}{12} \quad \frac{1}{2} = \frac{9}{18}$$

$\frac{1}{2}$ is equivalent to $\frac{2}{4}$ and $\frac{6}{12}$, but not equivalent to $\frac{12}{18}$.

So $\frac{12}{18}$ should be circled.

(1 mark)

Q4

| $\frac{1}{3}$ | $\frac{1}{9}$ | $\frac{1}{15}$ |

| $\frac{3}{27}$ | $\frac{3}{9}$ | $\frac{2}{30}$ |

(2 marks for matching all three correctly. Otherwise 1 mark for matching one pair correctly.)

Q5

To get from 5 to 10, you multiply by 2. So multiply the numerator by 2 as well:

$\frac{3}{5} = \frac{6}{10}$ *(1 mark)*

To get from 4 to 1, you divide by 4. So divide the denominator by 4 as well:

$\frac{4}{28} = \frac{1}{7}$ *(1 mark)*

Pages 38-40 — Ordering Fractions

Q1

The first arrow is pointing to $\frac{3}{10}$ *(1 mark)*

The second arrow is pointing to $\frac{9}{10}$ *(1 mark)*

Q2

The fractions all have the same denominator, so the largest is the one with the largest numerator:

$\frac{8}{9}$ *(1 mark)*

Q3

The fractions all have the same denominator, so compare the numerators to put them in order:

$\frac{4}{17}, \frac{9}{17}, \frac{12}{17}, \frac{15}{17}$ *(1 mark)*

Q4

$\frac{1}{5} = \frac{4}{20}$ and $\frac{7}{10} = \frac{14}{20}$

In order, this is $\frac{3}{20}, \frac{4}{20}, \frac{14}{20}$.

So the correct order is:

$\frac{3}{20}, \frac{1}{5}, \frac{7}{10}$

(2 marks for the correct answer. Otherwise 1 mark for putting the fractions over the same denominator.)

Q5

Find equivalent fractions so that they all have the same denominator (12):

$\frac{2}{3} = \frac{8}{12}$ and $\frac{5}{6} = \frac{10}{12}$

In order, this is $\frac{7}{12}, \frac{8}{12}, \frac{10}{12}$.

So the correct order is:

$\frac{7}{12}, \frac{2}{3}, \frac{5}{6}$

(2 marks for the correct answer. Otherwise 1 mark for putting the fractions over the same denominator.)

Q6

Find equivalent fractions so that they all have the same denominator (16):

$\frac{1}{2} = \frac{8}{16}$ and $\frac{5}{8} = \frac{10}{16}$

In order, this is:

$\frac{10}{16}, \frac{9}{16}, \frac{8}{16}, \frac{3}{16}$.

So the correct order is:

$\frac{5}{8}, \frac{9}{16}, \frac{1}{2}, \frac{3}{16}$

(2 marks for the correct answer. Otherwise 1 mark for putting the fractions over the same denominator.)

Pages 41-42 — Using Fractions

Q1

$\frac{1}{2}$ of $24 = 24 \div 2$
$= \mathbf{12}$ *(1 mark)*

Q2

$\frac{1}{3}$ of $18 = 18 \div 3$
$= \mathbf{6}$ *(1 mark)*

$\frac{1}{9}$ of $18 = 18 \div 9$
$= \mathbf{2}$ *(1 mark)*

Q3

$\frac{1}{5}$ of $35 = 35 \div 5$
$= 7$

So 7 go through the hoop, and $35 - 7 = \mathbf{28}$ do not go through the hoop.
(2 marks for the correct answer. Otherwise 1 mark for correct working.)

Q4

$\frac{1}{3}$ of $27 = 27 \div 3 = 9$

So $\frac{2}{3}$ of 27 is $9 \times 2 = \mathbf{18}$
(2 marks for the correct answer. Otherwise 1 mark for correct working.)

Q5

$\frac{1}{5}$ of $50 = 50 \div 5 = 10$

So $\frac{3}{5}$ of 50 is $10 \times 3 = \mathbf{30}$
(2 marks for the correct answer. Otherwise 1 mark for correct working.)

$\frac{1}{10}$ of $50 = 50 \div 10 = 5$

So $\frac{7}{10}$ of 50 is $5 \times 7 = \mathbf{35}$
(2 marks for the correct answer. Otherwise 1 mark for correct working.)

Answers

Pages 43-44 — Adding and Subtracting Fractions

Q1 $\frac{1}{3}+\frac{1}{3}=\frac{1+1}{3}=\frac{2}{3}$ *(1 mark)*

Q2 $\frac{9}{10}-\frac{8}{10}=\frac{9-8}{10}=\frac{1}{10}$
(1 mark)

Q3 $\frac{1}{5}+\frac{2}{5}=\frac{1+2}{5}=\frac{3}{5}$ *(1 mark)*

Q4 $\frac{1}{4}=\frac{4}{16}$
So $\frac{1}{4}+\frac{1}{16}=\frac{4}{16}+\frac{1}{16}$
$=\frac{4+1}{16}=\frac{5}{16}$
(2 marks for the correct answer. Otherwise 1 mark for correct working.)

Q5 $\frac{1}{2}=\frac{5}{10}$
So $\frac{8}{10}-\frac{1}{2}=\frac{8}{10}-\frac{5}{10}$
$=\frac{8-5}{10}=\frac{3}{10}$
(2 marks for the correct answer. Otherwise 1 mark for correct working.)

Q6 $\frac{3}{8}=\frac{6}{16}$
So $\frac{3}{8}+\frac{3}{16}=\frac{6}{16}+\frac{3}{16}$
$=\frac{6+3}{16}=\frac{9}{16}$
(2 marks for the correct answer. Otherwise 1 mark for correct working.)

Pages 45-46 — Fractions and Decimals

Warm up

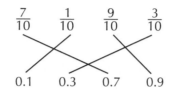

Q1 0.65 is 65 hundredths, which is $\frac{65}{100}$ *(1 mark)*

Q2 $\frac{2}{100}$ is 2 hundredths, which is **0.02** *(1 mark)*

Q3 0.11 is 11 hundredths, which is $\frac{11}{100}$ *(1 mark)*

Q4 $\frac{3}{25}=\frac{12}{100}$
$\frac{12}{100}$ is 12 hundredths, which is **0.12**
(2 marks for the correct answer. Otherwise 1 mark for correct working.)

Q5 $\frac{2}{50}=\frac{4}{100}$
$\frac{4}{100}$ is 4 hundredths, which is **0.04**
(2 marks for the correct answer. Otherwise 1 mark for correct working.)

Page 47 — Percentages

Q1 **75%** *(1 mark)*

Q2 $28\div100=\mathbf{0.28}$ *(1 mark)*
$0.37\times100=\mathbf{37\%}$ *(1 mark)*

Q3 $\frac{7}{100}$ *(1 mark)*

Q4 Jose's score was $\frac{86}{100}$ which is **86%**. *(1 mark)*

Pages 48-49 — Percentage Problems

Q1 $100-65=35$
So **35%** ordered coffee.
(1 mark)

Q2 $55+15=70$
$100-70=30$
So **30%** are pink. *(1 mark)*

Q3 10% of $80=80\div10=\mathbf{8}$
(1 mark)

Q4 10% of $750=750\div10=\mathbf{75}$
(1 mark)

Q5 10% of $20=20\div10=2$
60% of $20=6\times2=\mathbf{12}$
(2 marks for the correct answer. Otherwise 1 mark for correct working.)

Q6 10% of $500=500\div10=50$
40% of $500=4\times50=\mathbf{200}$
(2 marks for the correct answer. Otherwise 1 mark for correct working.)

Answers

Section Four — Measure

Pages 50-51 — Units and Conversions

Warm up
grams, kilograms

Q1
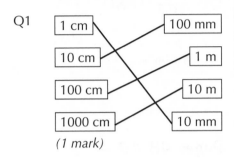
(1 mark)

Q2 1 kg = 1000 g
3 kg = 3 × 1000
= **3000 g** *(1 mark)*

Q3 1000 m = 1 km
3500 m = 3500 ÷ 1000
= **3.5 km** *(1 mark)*

Q4 1 gallon = 8 pints
7 gallons = 7 × 8
= **56 pints** *(1 mark)*

Q5 12 inches = 1 foot
96 inches = 96 ÷ 12
= **8 feet** *(1 mark)*

6 feet = 6 × 12 = 72 inches
So 6 feet 10 inches
= 72 + 10 = **82 inches**
(1 mark)

Pages 52-53 — Reading Scales

Q1 **7.5 cm** *(1 mark)*

Q2 Difference between two
numbered marks = 1 kg
There are 2 divisions between
each numbered mark so each
division is 1 ÷ 2 = 0.5 kg.
So the mass of the kettle is
2 + 0.5 = **2.5 kg** *(1 mark)*

Q3 Difference between two
numbered marks = 100 g
There are 4 divisions between
each numbered mark so each
division is 100 ÷ 4 = 25 g.
So 125 g is one division
above 100 g.

```
├─┬─┬─┬─┬─▲─┬─┬─┬─┤
0         100 g↑      200 g
```
(1 mark)

Q4 Difference between two
numbered marks = 100 ml.
There are 5 divisions between
each numbered mark so each
division is 100 ÷ 5 = 20 ml.
2 divisions = 2 × 20 = 40 ml
Volume = 100 + 40
= **140 ml** *(1 mark)*

Q5 Height of Dog A = 80 cm
Height of Dog B = 50 cm
80 – 50 = **30 cm**
*(2 marks for the correct
answer. Otherwise 1 mark
for finding the correct heights
for the dogs.)*

Pages 54-55 — Calculating with Measures

Q1 Difference between two
numbered marks = 50 ml
There are 5 divisions between
each numbered mark so each
division is 50 ÷ 5 = 10 ml.
2 divisions = 2 × 10 = 20 ml
Volume = 50 + 20 = 70 ml
Amount of water left
= 70 – 25 = **45 ml** *(1 mark)*

Q2 1 m = 100 cm
2 m = 2 × 100 = 200 cm
So 200 + 50 = **250 cm**
(1 mark)

10 mm = 1 cm
80 mm = 80 ÷ 10 = 8 cm
So 2 + 8 = **10 cm** *(1 mark)*

Q3 1000 m = 1 km
Each day Jean runs 2000 m
= 2000 ÷ 1000 = 2 km.
So she runs 2 × 7 = **14 km** in
a week.
*(2 marks for the correct
answer. Otherwise 1 mark
for correct working.)*

Q4 Mass of 3 small bags:
3 × 400 = 1200 g
Mass of 1 large bag:
2 kg = 2 × 1000 = 2000 g
Total mass = 1200 + 2000
= **3200 g**
*(2 marks for the correct
answer. Otherwise 1 mark
for correct working.)*

Q5 3 × 200 = **600 ml** *(1 mark)*

5 × 600 = 3000 ml
1000 ml = 1 litre
3000 ml = 3000 ÷ 1000
= **3 litres**
*(2 marks for the correct
answer. Otherwise 1 mark if
answer is given in millilitres.)*

Answers

Pages 56-57 — Money

Warm up

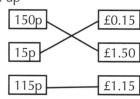

Q1 $470 \div 100 = $ **£4.70** *(1 mark)*

     $10.20 \times 100 = $ **1020p**
(1 mark)

Q2 $25p + 85p = 110p$
$110 \div 100 = $ **£1.10** *(1 mark)*

Q3
```
      7 5
  ×     9
    6 7 5  = 675p
    6 4
```
$675 \div 100 = $ **£6.75** *(1 mark)*

Q4   Three pencils cost:
```
      5 5
  ×     3
    1 6 5
    1 1
```
     $= 165p$

     $165 \div 100 = $ £1.65

     Total cost:
```
    2 . 3 0
  + 1 . 6 5
    3 . 9 5  = £3.95
```
*(2 marks for the correct
answer. Otherwise 1 mark
for finding the cost of three
pencils.)*

Q5   In total he spends:
```
    1 7 . 5 0
  +  2 . 1 0
    1 9 . 6 0  = £19.60
```
```
     3  9
        10  10
    4 0 . 0 0
  - 1 9 . 6 0
    2 0 . 4 0
```
He has **£20.40** left over.
*(2 marks for the correct
answer. Otherwise 1 mark
for finding how much Moeen
spends.)*

Pages 58-60 — Time

Q1   **21:55** *(1 mark)*

Q2   **03:40** *(1 mark)*

     $03:40 + 25$ minutes
$= $ **04:05** *(1 mark)*

Q3 $7 \times 4 = 28$
There are **28** days in 4 weeks.
(1 mark)

```
      6 0
  ×    7
    4 2 0
```
There are **420** seconds in
7 minutes. *(1 mark)*

Q4 $17:30 + 30$ minutes $= 18:00$
$18:00 + 45$ minutes $= 18:45$
$30 + 45 = $ **75 minutes**
(1 mark)

Q5 $12:53 + 7$ mins $= 13:00$
$13:00 + 48$ mins $= 13:48$
$7 + 48 = $ **55 minutes** *(1 mark)*

Q6 $19:20 + 40$ minutes $= 20:00$
$20:00 + 15$ minutes $= 20:15$

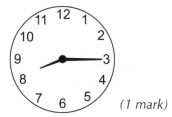

(1 mark)

Q7   Subtract 1 hour $= 60$ mins:
$125 - 60 = 65$ mins
Subtract another 60 mins:
$65 - 60 = 5$ mins
After subtracting 2 hours
there are 5 minutes left, so
the film is **2 hours 5 minutes**
(1 mark)

     $18:25 + 2$ hours $= 20:25$
$20:25 + 5$ mins $= $ **20:30**
(1 mark)

Pages 61-62 — Perimeter

Q1 $10 + 8 + 8 + 6 + 10 + 6$
$= $ **48 cm** *(1 mark)*

Q2   The shortest side is 3 cm.
The longest side is 5 cm.
So the perimeter is:
$3 + 5 + 3 + 5 = $ **16 cm**
(1 mark)

Q3   It is a regular hexagon so all
sides will be the same length.
$6 \times 4 = $ **24 m** *(1 mark)*

Q4   Missing side $= 8 - 5 = 3$ cm
Perimeter $= 4 + 5 + 2 + 8 + 6$
$+ 3 = $ **28 cm** *(1 mark)*

Q5   Missing side $= 8 - 3 - 3$
$= 2$ cm
Perimeter $= 8 + 1 + 3 + 4 + 2$
$+ 4 + 3 + 1 = $ **26 cm** *(1 mark)*

Page 63 — Area

Q1   There are 7 full squares and
2 half squares.
So total area $= 7 + \frac{1}{2} + \frac{1}{2} = $
8 m² *(1 mark)*

7 squares are more than half
covered by the shape.

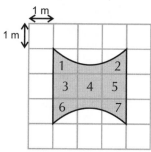

Its total area is about **7 m²**.
(1 mark)

Q2   A, B and C all cover
4 squares. **D** should be
circled as it only covers
3 and a half squares.
(1 mark)

Answers

Q3   E.g:

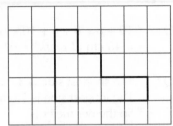

(1 mark for any shape with an area of 7 cm².)

Pages 64-65 — Areas of Squares and Rectangles

Warm up
Area = length × width

Q1   Area = 4 × 3 = **12 cm²**
(1 mark)

Q2   Area of rectangle A:
8 × 3 = **24 cm²** *(1 mark)*

Area of rectangle B:
= 6 × 12 = **72 mm²** *(1 mark)*

Q3   The length and width are the same for a square.
So the area is 6 × 6 = **36 cm²**
(1 mark)

Q4   Length × 5 = 30
Length = 30 ÷ 5 = **6 m**
(1 mark)

Q5   8 × width = 56
Width = 56 ÷ 8
        = **7 m** *(1 mark)*

Pages 66-67 — Volume

Q1

15 cubes = **15 cm³** *(1 mark)*

12 cubes = **12 cm³** *(1 mark)*

Q2   Volume of cube
= 4 × 4 × 4 = **64 cm³**
(1 mark)

Volume of cuboid
= 6 × 4 × 2 = **48 cm³**
(1 mark)

Q3   Volume of cuboid A:
2 × 3 × 6 = 36 cm³

Volume of cuboid B:
2 × 2 × 8 = 32 cm³

Volume of cuboid C:
3 × 3 × 3 = 27 cm³

Volume of cuboid D:
12 × 3 × 1 = 36 cm³

A and **D** have the same volume.
(2 marks for the correct answer. Otherwise 1 mark for working out any two volumes correctly.)

Q4   Volume of X = 5 × 3 × 2
= **30 cm³** *(1 mark)*

Volume of Y = 7 × 6 × 2
= **84 cm³** *(1 mark)*

Volume of Z = 8 × 5 × 3
= **120 cm³** *(1 mark)*

Section Five — Geometry

Pages 68-69 — Measuring Angles

Q1

— reflex angle

— acute angle

— obtuse angle
(1 mark)

Q2   **145°** *(1 mark for any answer between 143° and 147°.)*

Q3

75°

(1 mark for drawing an angle between 73° and 77°.)

Q4   **115°** *(1 mark for any answer between 113° and 117°.)*

Q5   The acute angle is the smallest angle in the quadrilateral.
35° *(1 mark for any answer between 33° and 37°.)*

Answers

Pages 70-71 — Angles

Warm up

The angles on a straight line add up to **180°**.
The angles around a point add up to **360°**.
The angles in a right angle add up to **90°**.

Q1   A = 90° − 30° = **60°** *(1 mark)*

       B = 90° − 55° = **35°** *(1 mark)*

Q2   L = 180° − 120° = **60°**
       (1 mark)

       M = 180° − 40° − 45° = **95°**
       (1 mark)

Q3   P = 360° − 145° = **215°**
       (1 mark)

       Q = 360° − 110° − 120°
          = **130°** *(1 mark)*

Q4   Y = 360° − 28° = **332°**
       (1 mark)

       reflex *(1 mark)*

Pages 72-73 — 2D Shapes

Warm up

Q1

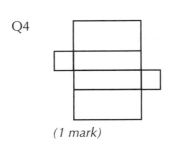

Trapezium

Parallelogram

Rhombus

(1 mark)

Q2   **Hexagon** *(1 mark)*

       Octagon *(1 mark)*

Q3   It has 3 equal angles and 3 equal sides — **Equilateral**
All sides and angles are different — **Scalene**
It has 2 equal sides and 2 equal angles — **Isosceles**
(1 mark)

Q4

(1 mark)

Pages 74-75 — 3D Shapes

Warm up
     Prism
     Cylinder
     Cuboid

Q1   **Cone** *(1 mark)*

       Pyramid (or **Square-Based Pyramid**) *(1 mark)*

Q2   **Cylinder** *(1 mark)*

       Cuboid *(1 mark)*

Q3

(1 mark)

Q4

(1 mark)

Q5

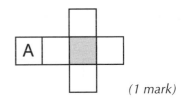

A

(1 mark)

Pages 76-77 — Coordinates

Q1   Point A: **(2, 1)**
       Point B: **(5, 4)**
       (1 mark)

Q2

(1 mark)

Q3   Point M: **(−4, 1)**
       Point N: **(−2, −3)**
       (1 mark)

Q4

(1 mark)

Q5   **(−3, 3)** *(1 mark)*

Answers

Pages 78-80 — Reflection

Q1

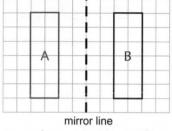

mirror line

(1 mark)

Q2

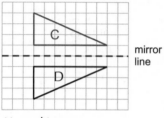

mirror line

(1 mark)

Q3

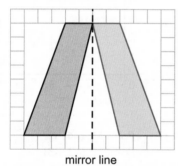

mirror line

(1 mark)

Q4

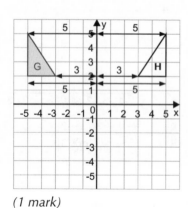

(1 mark)

Q5

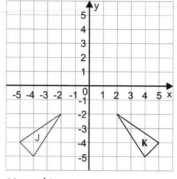

(1 mark)

Q6

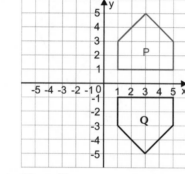

(1 mark)

Pages 81-82 — Translation

Warm up

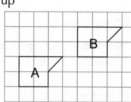

Q1

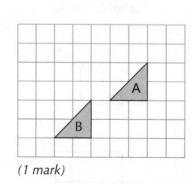

(1 mark)

Q2

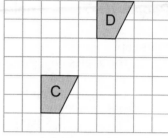

(1 mark)

Q3

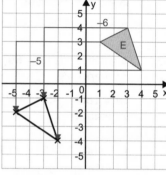

(1 mark)

Q4

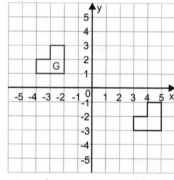

(1 mark)

Answers

Section Six —
Statistics

Pages 83-85 —
Tables

Warm up

Flavour	Ready Salted	Salt and Vinegar	Beef
Number of bags sold	35	12	15

Q1   **15** *(1 mark)*

Number of children travelling by car = 1
Number of children travelling by bus = 10
Number of children travelling by train = 3
1 + 10 + 3 = **14** *(1 mark)*

Q2   52 cakes were sold on Monday.
23 cakes were sold on Friday.
52 − 23 = **29** *(1 mark)*

Q3   The last bus to arrive in Millum before 9:00 am arrives at 8:57 am.
This bus leaves Rexhill at **8:20 am** *(1 mark)*

Q4   The last train to arrive in Stow on Rye before 15:10 arrives at 15:00.
This train leaves Ashdown at **13:20** *(1 mark)*

The 14:25 train from Hillgate arrives in Park Grove at **15:35** *(1 mark)*

The 12:40 train from Ashdown gets to Stanton at 13:25.
12:40 + 20 mins = 13:00
13:00 + 25 mins = 13:25 so it takes 20 + 25 = **45 minutes** *(1 mark)*

Pages 86-87 —
Pictograms and Bar Charts

Q1
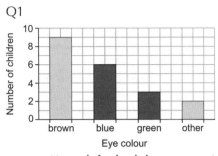

(1 mark for both bars correct)

Q2

David	▢ ▢ ▯
Isobel	▢ ▢ ▢ ▢ ▯

(1 mark)

David ate 2 + 2 + 1 = 5 pieces of fruit. So Isobel ate 9 − 5 = **4** more *(1 mark)*

Q3   Number of hotdogs = 11
Number of salads = 8
11 + 8 = **19**
(2 marks for the correct answer. Otherwise 1 mark for finding the number of hotdogs sold and the number of salads sold.)

Q4   Each circle shows 4 animals.
Each half circle shows 4 ÷ 2 = 2 animals.
Each quarter circle shows 4 ÷ 4 = 1 animal.
There are:
10 whole circles = 10 × 4 = 40
2 half circles = 2 × 2 = 4
1 quarter circle = 1
So in total there are 40 + 4 + 1 = **45** dogs, cats and fish
(2 marks for the correct answer. Otherwise 1 mark for correct working.)

Pages 88-89 —
Line Graphs

Q1   **80 cm** *(1 mark)*

5 *(1 mark)*

At age 3 Sarah was 90 cm tall.
At age 7 Sarah was 110 cm tall.
110 − 90 = **20 cm**
(2 marks for the correct answer. Otherwise 1 mark for finding Sarah's height at the ages of 3 and 7.)

Q2   **150** *(1 mark)*

2005 *(1 mark)*

In 2010, Cragston = 300 and Teignton = 250.
300 + 250 = **550**
(2 marks for the correct answer. Otherwise 1 mark for finding the populations of each town in 2010.)

Pages 90-93 —
Practice Test 2

Q1   Subtract the numbers in the tens places: 7 − 3 = 4.
So 672 − 30 = **642** *(1 mark)*

Q2   Area = length × width
8 × 5 = **40 cm²** *(1 mark)*

Q3 $9^2 = 9 × 9 = $ **81** *(1 mark)*

Q4   1 cm = 10 mm
7 cm = 7 × 10 = **70 mm** *(1 mark)*

1000 ml = 1 litre
8000 ml = 8000 ÷ 1000 = **8 litres** *(1 mark)*

Q5   CCXV = 100 + 100 + 10 + 5 = **215** *(1 mark)*

Answers

Q6

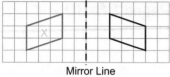

Mirror Line

(1 mark)

Q7 $\frac{1}{6} = \frac{2}{12} = \frac{10}{60}$

(2 marks for both correct values. Otherwise 1 mark for one correct value.)

Q8
```
  1 2 7 3
×       6
  7 6 3 8  (1 mark)
  1 4 1
```

Q9 All of the numbers have the same digit in the ones place so look at the tenths places.

2.09 has a 0 in the tenths place so it's the smallest.

2.78 has a 7 in the tenths place so it's the largest.

2.46 and 2.49 both have a 4 in the tenths place so look at the hundredths places.
2.46 has 6 in the hundredths place and 2.49 had 9 in the hundredths place.
So 2.46 is smaller than 2.49

The correct order is:
2.09, 2.46, 2.49, 2.78
(1 mark)

Q10
```
    3 5
×     3
  1 0 5
  1 1
```
3 lemons cost 105p = £1.05
```
  1 . 0 5
+ 1 . 3 5
  2 . 4 0
        1
```
So 3 lemons and a pineapple will cost **£2.40**
(2 marks for the correct answer. Otherwise 1 mark for showing some correct working.)

Q11 The missing side and the 6 cm side are opposite the 9 cm side. So the missing side is: 9 − 6 = 3 cm
The total perimeter is 9 + 10 + 6 + 5 + 3 + 5 = **38 cm**
(2 marks for the correct answer. Otherwise 1 mark for finding the length of the missing side or finding the perimeter without the missing side.)

Q12 6 out of 10 sections are shaded which is
$\frac{6}{10} = \frac{60}{100} = 60\%$ *(1 mark)*

Q13 **165°** *(1 mark for an answer between 163° and 167°)*

35 mm *(1 mark for an answer between 33 mm and 37 mm)*

Q14 The 13:40 bus from Lawes gets to Attwood at 14:25.
From 13:40 to 14:00 is 20 minutes. From 14:00 to 14:25 is 25 minutes.
20 + 25 = **45 minutes**
(2 marks for the correct answer. Otherwise 1 mark for finding what time he will get to Attwood.)

MLBW22